JET
WARPLANES

JET
WARPLANES

MICHAEL J. H. TAYLOR

BISON BOOKS CORP

This edition published 1984 by
Bison Books Corp.
17 Sherwood Place
Greenwich, CT 06830
USA

ISBN 0 86124 165 7

Printed in Hong Kong

CONTENTS

In 1982 and 1983, Bison Books published *Jet Fighter* and *Jet Bombers* respectively. Because of their international popularity, the decision has been taken to publish this new single volume which combines both.

Since the earliest recorded aviation feats, flight performance has been restricted most critically by the types of power plant available to aircraft builders and would-be aviators. In centuries long past, those persons that longed to fly with the birds quickly discovered, as they leapt from towers and high walls, that man's muscles used to flap artificial wings were insufficient for the job. Even the renowned inventor, Leonardo da Vinci, could not progress the art of flying. Many of his machines were designed to

work as ornithopters, with the pilot of each intended to work a series of levers, pulleys and harnesses to flap wings or move other propulsive devices.

The 18th century saw the birth of aviation proper, when at last man left the ground in hot-air and then hydrogen balloons. But there was a price to be paid for such simple forms of aircraft. While actual flying was possible, the lack of a suitable power plant to generate propulsion meant that drifting at the mercy of the winds was all that could be achieved. Even with the invention of the steerable airship (dirigible), fitted with a steam, gas or electric motor initially, control over the intended flight was far from adequate.

For a period in the 19th century it appeared likely that refined steam engines would allow man to conquer heavier-than-air powered flight. In the middle of the century, so certain of a happy outcome were some designers that plans were made to establish an airline to transport passengers by steam-plane to many far off corners of our planet. This idea, as aviation history records, came to nothing. The fact that no steam-powered aeroplane of this century made anything beyond a brief, if eventful, leap from the ground was due almost entirely to the heavy power plant, for many of the airframes were indeed airworthy.

The invention of the petrol internal combustion engine changed all this, allowing

INTRODUCTION

would-be aviators to build aircraft with engines of sufficient power, yet light enough to allow sustained flight. The piston engine reigned supreme until after World War Two and today remains ideal for most small aircraft. Development of the piston engine in its varied forms during the first four decades of the 20th century allowed over higher officially ratified speeds to be set; the 34mph achieved by Paul Tissandier's Wright biplane in 1909 paved the way for the 126mph Deperdussin monoplane of 1913 and the impressive 469mph attained by the Messerschmitt Bf 209 in 1939. But even with today's technical advances, the highest speed yet achieved by a piston-engined aeroplane stands at only 517.06mph, set by a

modified North American P-51D Mustang in 1983.

By the outbreak of World War Two, however, a new form of power plant had germinated that eventually allowed (decades later) operational aircraft capable of speeds in excess of three times the speed of sound. This was the turbojet engine, used to early effect by Britain and Germany in subsonic warplanes that flew in the skies over Europe from 1944. Such was the potential of jet aircraft that, postwar, nations with important air forces were forced to spend vast sums of money replacing piston warplanes.

During the same war the rocket motor had also become a rational choice of power plant for aircraft, both Germany and Japan

General Dynamics F-16 Fighting Falcon of the USAF.

deploying operational aircraft using this form of power. The early development of rocket planes is also detailed in this book. However, although development of rocket planes continued after the war and rocket-powered aircraft subsequently managed speeds of up to 4534mph, this form of power plant has never been adopted as the main power source for a postwar operational aircraft. Today the turbojet and related turbofan, turboprop and turboshaft remain the unrivalled power plants of modern high performance and large aircraft.

1: AGAINST THE ODDS

Turbojet and turbofan-powered fighters of today are man-made meteors of destruction; the most formidable are capable of speeds of more than two-and-a-half times the speed of sound and possess incredible rates of climb of approximately 50,000 feet per minute. In a secondary attack role, the same fighters can carry bombs and other weapons equivalent in weight to that carried by some of the heaviest bombers of World War II. All this is a far cry from the first jet fighters that appeared in operational units in 1944.

It seems incongruous that jet fighters were streaking in the skies of Europe during World War II, but no more so than the USAF finding in some situations during the Vietnam conflict that high-technology multi-million dollar jet fighter-bombers were of less use than veteran piston-engined aircraft. Such are the unexpected demands of war. What is surprising is that despite the appalling amount of time wasted in getting jets into service during World War II, between the time the Luftwaffe received its first jets and its capitulation Germany produced more than ten 'jet aces.' Oberstleutnant Heinz Bär of JV 44, the Luftwaffe's elite jet squadron formed in early 1945 by Adolf Galland, personally boasted no fewer than 16 'jet kills' amongst his overall war total of 220 victories.

It is a common misconception to believe that jet fighters were the end result for Germany and Britain of frantic experiments prior to the outbreak of war, to lay the foundations for the ultimate warplane. Far from it. Whilst it is true that there were those in both countries that had faith in the gas turbine engine as a power plant for aircraft, official government views were far from encouraging, as is now explained.

Three names are synonymous with the early development of the turbojet engine and turbojet-powered aircraft, those of Whittle, von Ohain and Heinkel. But whilst Whittle was the first to run a turbojet engine intended as a power plant for an aircraft, the Germans were the first to marry engine and airframe. This came about not because the German Air Ministry had any more faith in the concept than the British Air Ministry, but because von Ohain had the help of an airframe manufacturer whereas Whittle had not.

In Germany in the 1930s Ernst Heinkel was the head of a major aircraft manufacturing company, Ernst Heinkel Flugzeugwerke GmbH. He believed that no piston-engined aircraft would ever exceed around

Above: the Heinkel He 178, which was the world's first jet-powered aircraft, lifts off.

Overleaf: this Gloster F.9/40 Meteor was powered by Rolls-Royce Trent turboprops.

800 km/h (500 mph). A similar view was taken by eminent persons in Britain. Typical was the stance adopted by a former British Director of Scientific Research in a lecture he gave in early 1937, when he stated that higher speeds could be attained only if a new 'prime mover' was invented producing much greater thrust, and that there was no inkling of such a power plant and man would probably never exceed 965 km/h (600 mph) level speed in an aeroplane. By the time of this lecture Whittle and the staff of Power Jets Ltd had already run the first Whittle turbojet engine!

Going further back to 1926, a Briton named Dr A A Griffith expounded his ideas on gas turbine engines for aeroplanes. He was then employed at the Royal Aircraft Establishment (RAE). In the same year a young man named Frank Whittle joined the RAF College at Cranwell as a Flight Cadet. Two years later an article entitled *Speculation* appeared in the college journal, in which Whittle gave an outline of the equations for a gas turbine engine. While at the Central Flying School in 1929 he had a meeting with officials at the Air Ministry, who it is said considered his ideas impracticable. Sensibly, Whittle took out a patent to protect his brainchild but then settled down to his chosen career, although he made further attempts to interest the Air Ministry. One outcome of these meetings was that the

Ministry was coerced into supporting limited research at the RAE, which in the event achieved virtually nothing.

If one looks at the list of directors for the later-formed company Power Jets (Research and Development) Ltd, three of the names are Whittle, J C B Tinling and R D Williams. Tinling and Williams had been RAF officers and knew of Whittle's work. By 1935 they had together established an engineering business and felt in a position to approach Whittle with a proposition that was to lead eventually to the greatest sustained leap forward in aviation technology since the invention of the internal combustion engine. They suggested that for a share of the profits they would attempt to find the necessary finance to build a Whittle engine. A company named Power Jets Ltd was formed, with the intention of producing an engine suited for a revolutionary stratospheric mailplane. About the same time the Air Ministry was taking more interest in the type of engine, via the RAE, having changed its mind about the jet engine's possible military applications.

Whittle began serious design in mid-1935 and the first Whittle engine with a centrifugal compressor, known as the W/U Type, was built by the British Thomson-Houston Company, based at Rugby, to a Power Jets order. This engine was the first gas turbine engine to be designed for an aircraft and, amid great excitement, was started up for the first time on 12 April 1937, several months prior to the von Ohain engine in Germany.

Now work really began in earnest. Soon the W/U was being modified and reconstructed, running again in very different form in October 1938. The W/U was

Above: the Power Jets W1 engine mounted on a test stand at Lutterworth, Leicestershire.

Whittle's only engine until the W1X was started up in December 1940 and all jet development up to this time by Power Jets was carried out on this single unit. In March 1938 the Air Ministry placed a contract for a Whittle engine. The Ministry later awarded Gloster a contract to produce an airframe to carry the engine under specification E.28/39.

Meanwhile in Germany by the mid-1930s unusual experiments were also taking place. As mentioned earlier, Ernst Heinkel was a leader in the development of the German turbojet engine, but he also had an important role to play in the development of a rocket motor for aircraft. Indeed Heinkel was initially involved with rocket power and saw a great future for this type of power plant. For Heinkel, what his rocket-powered aircraft experiments proved was that a rear-exhausting power plant was feasible for aeroplanes, against the official German Air Ministry viewpoint. But, as if by retribution for not toeing the line, his engines never achieved any major production success and other companies more successfully exploited turbojet and rocket-powered aircraft for operational use with the Luftwaffe.

In late 1935 Ernst Heinkel met a young scientist named Wernher von Braun, who had been experimenting with rocket motors for the German Army at Kummers-dorf. Such was the eventual success of his experiments that between December of the following year and 1938 the 'whole show' was officially moved from Kummersdorf to

the new highly secret and much larger research establishment built for the Third Reich at Peenemünde, where the 'terror weapons' of World War II were developed.

Heinkel had not been requested to visit Kummersdorf to admire von Braun's work on artillery rocket motors, but to hear his ideas for a rocket-powered plane. Why Heinkel had been selected from all the heads of German airframe manufacturers to be approached can be explained easily. Firstly he had expounded openly his criticism of German engine manufacturers, who in his opinion were falling behind in technological progress when compared with the achievements being made in other European countries. Secondly von Braun had already tested rocket engines on a rig, which had rotated at great speed before exploding, and he now wanted one of the most modern aeroplane fuselages with which to continue his work towards a rocket plane, and Heinkel had such a fuselage.

At this time the Heinkel company had flown the prototype of its new He 112 single-seat monoplane fighter, a rival for the Messerschmitt Bf 109 for Luftwaffe orders and von Braun modestly wanted an He 112 fuselage. Luckily for him, he had approached the right man. Under intense secrecy Ernst Heinkel provided an He 112 fuselage, together with a number of Heinkel employees.

During the first weeks of 1936 von Braun tested his motor installed in the anchored fuselage, all trials being conducted for safety from behind a concrete wall screen. The liquid oxygen and alcohol tanks to fuel the motor were placed fore and aft of the cockpit. With von Braun behind the wall was Erich Warsitz, who had already volun-

teered to fly a rocket-powered plane when developed. What he must have felt when one explosion followed another can only be speculated upon, but, as will be explained, Warsitz was later very important to rocket and turbojet-powered aircraft research and development.

By February von Braun felt that he had developed the motor to a point where it was safe for onlookers to stand beside the fuselage while the motor was run and he and Warsitz did this daring act to impress Ernst Heinkel. Luckily it did impress him, for von Braun was soon in need of a second fuselage when the first had blown up with a motor during later tests. This too was subsequently destroyed. The third He 112 provided was a complete aircraft. Once with von Braun it had a rocket motor installed in the aft fuselage. It was envisioned that in this aircraft Warsitz was to attempt a few simple rocket motor tests while airborne, but it too exploded. Still Warsitz retained faith in the concept, and, after von Braun had extracted yet another He 112 out of Heinkel, he realised his dream.

In April 1937 the second complete He 112 took off under the power of its piston engine, but switched to rocket power once airborne. With tremendous acceleration the plane's speed rose. Then the cockpit became filled with fumes and Warsitz made an emergency crash landing. In the following period the repaired He 112 flew several times, eventually taking off under rocket power alone.

During 1937 von Braun released details of his experiments and those of others in the same field to the Air Ministry. A motor fed with a different fuel mixture had by then been produced by Walter. This motor was also tested in the He 112 and proved very successful. In fact the Walter motor was the forerunner of the type later installed in the operational Messerschmitt Me 163 Komet rocket interceptor.

Much to Ernst Heinkel's dismay, the aeroplane rocket motor concept was seen by German officials mainly as a RATO (rocket-assisted take-off) unit for heavily-laden bombers and not as the main power plant for an aeroplane. Whilst Heinkel also saw its use in this role, especially in view of his own bombers being built for the Luftwaffe, it went against his main line of thinking. What is more, he had eyes on the world speed record for aeroplanes. Therefore, he subsequently offered von Braun and Warsitz a purpose-built rocket plane airframe, made small enough to win the record by a wide margin. Naturally this was greeted with

great enthusiasm, and the He 176 was built. Aiming for 1,000 km/h, it was designed to have a pilot escape capsule in case of an emergency.

As time passed von Braun became deeply involved with artillery rockets at Peenemünde and began to show less interest in the He 176. Not so the pilot, Warsitz. When completed the He 176 was taken in sections to the research establishment and later went through a series of towed and taxi trials and then hops. Then in June 1939 Warsitz made a 50 second flight without mishap. The next flight was in front of Ernst Heinkel, Ernst Udet, Erhard Milch and other dignitaries. A stop-go attitude from the General Staff followed, with the He 176 and Warsitz in turn forbidden to fly.

It soon became clear that the General Staff saw the He 176 as little more than a toy, with perhaps some future in developed form as a vertically-launched rocket interceptor to destroy bombers. Heinkel was again frustrated. History records that in fact Germany did eventually develop several rocket-powered interceptors for use during World War II, although Heinkel did not get a look-in. One has already been mentioned, but another of great interest was the Bachem Ba 349 Natter, which was indeed vertically launched. As for the He 176, it was destroyed alongside the He 178 during an Allied bombing raid on Berlin, where it had been sent for the Air Museum.

The He 178 itself was the outcome of very different experiments which ran parallel with those of the He 176. In 1936 Ernst Heinkel had again been contacted about another new type of power plant. Contact had come from Professor Robert Pohl of the University of Göttingen. He explained that he had a 24-year-old colleague named Hans Joachim Pabst von Ohain who was working on the design of a turbojet engine. On later meeting von Ohain, Heinkel was most impressed with his theories. But, although a

Above: a rare photograph of the Gloster E.28/39 experimental jet aircraft during flight trials.

model had previously been produced for von Ohain by Bartels and Beckers garage, von Ohain was not an engineer and had spent most of his private money thus far.

In April von Ohain and his assistant Max Hahn joined the Heinkel company. They worked in a specially-prepared building well away from the main Heinkel manufacturing plant at Marienehe, to maintain strict secrecy. Ernst Heinkel was very enthusiastic about this project and allowed many of his best employees to work with von Ohain and Hahn, together with a number of new employees. In the event, much of the detail work on the engine was left to Hahn.

Development of the turbine and the combustion chamber for the hydrogen fuel took about a year and a half. Following a number of unsuccessful attempts to run the engine, the S.1 started up for the first time in September 1937, well after Whittle's engine in Britain. This engine was designed for developmental purposes only and had a thrust of just 80kg (176lb). It was followed by the S.2 with a thrust of 130kg (286lb). By the

spring of 1938 the remarkable S.3 engine had been developed, which was fed with petrol and was controllable. In fact two S.3 series engines were built.

The S.3 was based on a compressor/turbine arrangement, comprising an axial-flow inducer, axial-flow impeller and radial inflow turbine. In this the air from the axial-flow impeller was divided to the rear of the diffuser; some passed forward through the annular reverse-flow combustion chamber and the rest was directed rearward to mix with the combustion gases before entry into the turbine. Total weight of the unit was 360kg (794lb), and its frontal area was 0.68 sq m (7.3 sq ft). The latter figure was important as Heinkel intended it to be mounted inside a small-diameter fuselage. There was some disagreement as to this installation, as it was realised that the engine's possible 450kg (992lb) of thrust would be reduced significantly if a long air intake and jetpipe were adopted, as would be necessary with the engine in the fuselage. Nevertheless Heinkel won the day, the purpose-built turbojet-powered research aircraft was to be a single-engined type.

Prior to flying the purpose-built He 178, the S.3 was flight tested on another aircraft. Here there is some confusion. Ernst Heinkel recorded much later that the first S.3 was fitted to an He 118 for initial flight testing and this appears to be generally accepted. The He 118 was the Heinkel entry for the latest dive-bomber competition, which incidentally was won by the Junkers Ju 87. This seemingly unlikely choice of engine testbed may have resulted from its availability and/or its good ground clearance by virtue of having been expected to carry a large bomb under the fuselage. However others

Below: a Gloster F.9/40 prototype pictured at Farnborough, Hampshire, in 1944.

Right: a Power Jets W2 jet engine is pictured installed in the Gloster E.28/39 airframe.

that worked on this early engine mention its installation in an He 100 single-seat fighter. The He 100 was basically a development of the He 112, as used for the rocket plane experiments, and in some respects seems at first a more likely choice. With the He 118 the engine would have had to be mounted beneath the fuselage. Although it is possible that the He 100 was used after initial flights with the He 118, no certainty can be expressed. However the He 100 would have allowed Heinkel and the others to measure actual reductions in thrust due to the use of an air intake and a jetpipe of some length.

By the time that the He 178 airframe had been completed in secrecy, the first engine's turbine had burned out. As there were only two engines, the decision was made to fit the remaining S.3b engine to the He 178 without delay.

The He 178 was not dissimilar in many ways to the He 176, although there were important differences apart from engine type. The nose of the duralumin-constructed monocoque fuselage had a large air intake, through which air was directed under the cramped pilot's cockpit to the engine installed approximately level with the trailing-edge of the shoulder-mounted wooden wings. A long jetpipe of welded chrome steel exhausted out of the rear fuselage. As with the He 176, the tailwheel-type landing gear was retractable.

Naturally there was only one pilot suited to the job of flying the He 178, not least because Warsitz had already been the pilot during the earlier-mentioned testbed flights. Warsitz had shown exceptional faith in Heinkel's experimental aircraft and had flown all of the earlier rocket and turbojet trials with great fortitude. Even the General Staff, who had not exactly been at pains to praise Heinkel for his private-venture contributions to the advancement of German aviation, had recognized Warsitz's great courage. Indeed it had organized large payments for his hazardous flights. Nevertheless even Warsitz was not entirely happy with the choice of the Marienehe airfield for flight testing the He 178. For a start he considered the airfield too short. Yet to go elsewhere would break the secrecy of their work and could conceivably cause the premature termination of the whole project. Of course, one of the Air Ministry's complaints – that engines should be made by engine makers – had already been settled by

Heinkel, for he acquired a major interest in the Hirth-Motoren engine company after the death of Hellmuth Hirth in June 1938.

Taxiing trials with the He 178 began on 24 August 1939. Then on 27 August Warsitz climbed into the small cockpit and was soon streaking along the airfield. Suddenly the aircraft left the ground and powered its way upwards. Unlike his flight in the He 176, Warsitz stayed up for minutes rather than seconds, to record the first flight in the world of a turbojet-powered aeroplane. History had indeed been made and those watching the flight knew it.

Ernst Heinkel's enthusiasm for the group's achievement was not matched by the response of Ernst Udet of the German Air Ministry (RLM), who had been contacted directly. Heinkel wanted him to see the second flight of the He 178 and could not understand why there should be any delay whatsoever. Actually the reason was simple, for it was only hours before German forces were to invade Poland. It was not until 1 November that Udet, Milch and Lucht visited the airfield to see the He 178's second flight; Goering had not even turned up. That day the first flight was a disaster, as it had to be terminated immediately after take off because of a seized fuel pump. Within three hours the fault had been rectified and a full demonstration was put on. Although the officials showed little interest as they departed, at least Heinkel now had a clearer idea of what he was going to be up against if he was to proceed.

When the Allies took charge of documents following Germany's capitulation in 1945, references were found for an S.6 engine, which preceded the important S.8 or 109-001. This was merely a new designation given to the S.3b prior to the November flights and following modifications to the engine to raise static thrust to 590kg (1301lb). However it appears to have

achieved poor results due to an increase in weight to 420kg (929lb). It is interesting to note that despite Heinkel's early lead, the company produced only a very small number of von Ohain engines in the projected S.1, S.2, S.3, S.8 and S.11 series, whilst the ducted fan engines designed by Max Mueller (who joined Heinkel from Junkers) as the S.50 and S.60 remained projects, as did his S.40. Mueller's S.30 axial-flow engine, known as the 109-006, was intended for the He 280 but was abandoned for some unexplainable reason after very great progress had been made. As for the He 178, this was destroyed alongside the He 176 in Berlin.

Although other German turbojet engines are mentioned later in this book, it is interesting to note at this point that BMW began preliminary work on jet propulsion in 1934 and commenced design of its 109-003 engine in 1939, which ran in the summer of the following year. The 109-003 had a seven-stage axial compressor and an annular combustion chamber with 16 burners and was the first type of turbojet fitted to a prototype Messerschmitt Me 262. Similarly Professor Leist at Daimler-Benz first ran a 109-007 in the autumn of 1943, but work was eventually abandoned as the engine was seen to be too complex by the German Air Ministry. The -007 had many special features, including the compressor and ducted fan being mounted on two contra-rotating drums. By far the most successful turbojet of German origin was the Junkers Jumo 109-004. Junkers had begun development in 1937, having been encouraged to so do by the technical division at the Air Ministry, and within two years the design for a turbojet engine had been completed. Construction of the prototype Jumo 109-004 began in 1940 and the first was started up in November that year. By mid-1941 Junkers had a number of engines completed. Towards the end of 1941 the Jumo 004 was flight tested by a Messerschmitt Bf 110. At about that time certain modifications to the engine had been designed to produce the 109-004B, which was run in late 1942. Meanwhile on 18 July 1942, -004As had been used in a prototype Me 262.

In Britain Power Jets had used considerable ingenuity in developing its W1 engine for flight trials in the Gloster E.28/39 airframe and, by making use of spare W1 component parts and others that were considered below standard for the flight engine, the company produced a second engine as the non-airworthy W1X. Interestingly, the W1X was the first of the two engines to be started up. It was to be used to help Gloster prepare the installation for the airworthy W1 and so successful was it that the initial taxiing trials of the E.28/39 were made with the W1X installed.

At this point one of aviation's remarkable but unrecognised 'firsts' occurred. Although the engine had a rating of 454kg (1,000lb) thrust, for safety this was to be kept down to 390kg (860lb). The pilot for the E.28/39 was PEG Sayer, Gloster's Chief Test Pilot. On 7 April 1941 Sayer performed the first taxiing trial, but on the following day he made the first of a number of 'hop' flights, still with the W1X engine fitted. As in the earliest days of flying, 'hop' flights were not counted as true flights and therefore, although Britain's first turbojet-powered aeroplane had left the ground, it was not a recorded 'first.'

The E.28/39 was then dismantled and taken to Cranwell, where it was to make its first proper flight with the W1 engine fitted. No doubt Whittle was pleased with this location, as Cranwell was where the jet engine was conceived and now would be the place of its fulfilment. As for the W1X, it was sent to the General Electric Company in the United States of America in September 1941, where it helped that company develop its own engine to power the first US jet fighter.

At 7.40 pm on 15 May 1941 Sayer took off in the E.28/39, making a highly successful 17 minute flight in which a speed of 386 km/h (240 mph) was recorded. This marked the first flight of a turbojet-powered aircraft anywhere in the world outside Germany. So successful was the engine/airframe combination that flying was cleared for ten hours with only routine attention. In fact during 17 flights without failure, up to 28 May, this was marginally exceeded. Within one and a half months the W1 was run on a Special Category Test of 25 hours and then it was again flight tested.

Whilst the British Air Ministry had not shown very much initiative earlier, now that Britain was at war it took much greater interest in jet propulsion. Even before the E.28/39 had flown, the Air Ministry had placed contracts for new engines and a prototype twin-engined fighter as the F.9/40. In June 1940 Dr Harold Roxbee Cox was appointed Deputy Director of Scientific Research with responsibility for the development of gas turbine engines.

Up to then Power Jets' engines had been built by the British Thomson-Houston Company. The new W2 engine for the Air Ministry was to have a thrust of 726kg (1600lb) and it was optimistically hoped by the Air Ministry that large numbers of these engines and fighter aircraft airframes could be coming off production lines very quickly.

As Britain and Germany appeared to be on the verge of producing jet fighters in 1940, why did it take until 1944 to get them into service? The answer to this is in the following chapter, which covers the actual development of jet fighter prototypes and production aircraft. It is sufficient here to say that turbojet engine development did not keep pace with airframe development. Indeed, in Britain Power Jets had tremendous difficulty developing the W2, which suffered compressor surging, turbine blade failure and other problems. Meanwhile the Rover Company had tooled for production and had to sit by while the small band of Power Jets workers at Lutterworth struggled to solve the problems.

Rover itself attempted to rectify the faults by carrying out modifications to the engine, which actually achieved little. Soon strain between Rover and Power Jets showed, but in an epic moment of aviation history Rolls-Royce offered to take over Rovers' turbojet activities at Barnoldswick in exchange for its own tank engine factory at Nottingham. Of course Rolls-Royce were aware of what it was taking on, for it had already given some assistance to Power Jets. Rolls-Royce was now in the turbojet industry.

Virtually as soon as the agreement had been struck between Rover and Rolls-Royce, and before Rolls-Royce took over the Barnoldswick factory in early 1943, Rolls-Royce had converted a Vickers Wellington bomber into a flying testbed for the Whittle engine, which now carried the

designation W.2B/23 and had a thrust of 567kg (1250lb). The engine was mounted in the Wellington's tail, with the turret removed and 25 hours of flying was performed, from the end of 1942. A second Wellington was also modified for high-altitude work.

The initial Rolls-Royce version of the W.2B/23 passed its 100 hour test in April 1943, the same month as Rolls-Royce officially took over the Barnoldswick factory. This engine was capable of 771kg (1700lb) thrust. Production deliveries of the Welland engine, as it was now named, began in May 1944. Rolls-Royce had always expected Barnoldswick to be mainly a research and development establishment, with the bulk of production to take place at Newcastle-under-Lyme, and indeed only 100 or so engines were built there.

The Rolls-Royce Derwent engine, intended as a Welland replacement, was based on the Rover W.2B/26, itself modelled on a Power Jets direct-flow combustion engine. The W.2B/26 first ran in March 1942 and the Rolls-Royce Derwent I development ran in July 1943, giving a thrust of 907kg (2000lb). The company's Nene engine, which was designed and built in just five and a half months, first ran on 27 October 1944. It was designed to give a static thrust of 1814kg (4000lb) but was improved for flying at 2268kg (5000lb) thrust. An American-built Lockheed P-80 Shooting Star was adapted as this engine's testbed. Perhaps the oddest installation of the period was when a prototype Meteor was used to flight test the Rolls-Royce Trent engine, which was similar to the Derwent but drove a five-blade propeller.

As in Germany, once the advantages of the turbojet engine had been realized, other companies entered the field, the most important of which were de Havilland and Metropolitan-Vickers. The former began design of what became the H-1 or Goblin in April 1941, and by March 1943 the engine was flying in a prototype Meteor. On 20 September it powered the D.H.100 Vampire jet fighter prototype on its maiden flight. Metropolitan-Vickers started turbojet development much earlier, in fact in 1938, and by 1940 had designed its F.2 axial-flow turbojet engine. Flight tests in a converted Lancaster began on 29 June 1943, followed by tests in a prototype Meteor from 13 November. Thrust for the F.2/1 was 816kg (1800lb).

As for Power Jets Ltd., the company that had started the ball rolling in Britain, it be-came voluntarily state owned in 1944, thereafter being known as Power Jets (Research and Development) Ltd. On 1 July 1946 the roles of this company, which were purely research and developmental and not to manufacture, were passed to the National Gas Turbine Establishment, which also took over its buildings. The head of the former Power Jets organisation, Roxbee Cox, became head of this Establishment. It was the end of an era. Some say jet engine development began as long ago as 1910, when the Romanian Henri Coanda is said to have flown briefly in a biplane powered by a 50hp Clerget piston engine which drove a fan in a nose duct to produce thrust. It actually began with Whittle's experiments and was now a reality. Meanwhile in 1943 the development of the jet fighter was still in its infancy.

2: THE FIRST JET FIGHTERS

Heinkel was undoubtedly the prewar champion of the German turbojet engine and jet aeroplane and he should have been in a strong position to monopolize both during World war II. Although by 1939 some members of the RLM had adopted a more realistic approach to the development of the turbojet and turbojet-powered aircraft, in the main the ministry remained convinced that there was no real need, or future, for either. But, in order to hedge its bets, it had by then encouraged other engine makers to develop turbojets. It also unknowingly further usurped Heinkel by giving the company a rival in the airframe field. The latter was Messerschmitt AG, which as early as 1938 had been contracted to produce a preliminary design for a twin-engined jet plane. How serious the RLM was at that time in wanting such an aeroplane can perhaps be judged only by its reaction to the flights of the He 178. However the new aeroplane was seen merely as an engine test-bed. The Messerschmitt design was known as Project 1065. The reason that the RLM favored Messer-

schmitt was to be found partly in the fact that Heinkel kept its experiments a close secret until success had been achieved. This attitude seemed expedient to Ernst Heinkel, who considered his experiments always under threat of premature shut-down, but on the other hand must have gone some way in blinding the RLM to the advanced nature of his company's work, as well as building mistrust.

Although intended as a test-bed, Messerschmitt had been quick to point out the Project 1065's suitability as a prototype jet fighter. Heinkel was also working on the design of a prototype fighter and, like Project 1065, adopted a twin underwing jet engine arrangement. In the first half of 1940 Messerschmitt and Heinkel received contracts to produce a small number of flying and static test aircraft for fighter development, although official attitudes at the RLM, and especially those of Udet and Milch, remained virtually unchanged. Only after the Luftwaffe had received a 'bloody nose' during the Battle of Britain did the RLM realize once and for all that long term development of warplanes was going to be

essential; superior numbers had not won the day and there was not going to be a quick end to the war.

Heinkel appeared in a happier position than Messerschmitt by virtue of having two engines under development that were suited to the new aeroplane, now designated He 280. The first was von Ohain's S.8 centrifugal-flow engine; the second was Mueller's S.30 axial-flow engine. The first He 280 airframe was ready well before the S.8 engines and so it was used in a series of unpowered flights to gauge its aerodynamic qualities. An He 111 was used to tow the He 280 into the air. Many such unpowered flights were made while von Ohain and his team tried desperately to develop the S.8 to a point where sufficient thrust was produced to power the He 280 successfully and reliably.

Although the S.8 had been intended to produce 700kg (1543lb) of thrust, by the time 500kg (1102lb) was achieved the decision was made to fit two to the first He 280 airframe, under its straight but tapering wings. On 2 April 1941 the He 280V1 took off for the first time, with the nacelle panels for the engines removed as they tended to collect dangerous leaking fuel. This flight marked not only the first flight of a twin-engined turbojet-powered aircraft, but the

Overleaf: the Lockheed P-80 Shooting Star first flew on 8 January 1944, the XP-80A being pictured.

Below: Germany's Messerschmitt Me 262 saw combat service at the end of World War II.

Above: the Messerschmitt Me 262B-1a was a two-seat jet fighter trainer from which a nightfighter was developed.

first of a turbojet-powered machine intended as a fighter prototype. Often ignored is the fact that this flight *preceded* that of the experimental British Gloster E.28/39. What is more, the He 280 had several other very advanced features, which included a compressed air ejection seat for the pilot, and preempted the later Me 262 by having a tricycle landing gear from the outset.

About this time work also began on the new von Ohain S.11 engine (later known officially as the 109-011), intended to have a thrust of 1300kg (2866lb). The S.11 had a compressor with a diagonal-flow impeller stage and three axial-flow stages, an annular combustion chamber with 16 injection nozzles and an axial two-stage turbine with hollow blades. The exhaust nozzle was variable, with two positions. Contemporary reports suggest that the RLM saw the role of a new von Ohain engine as the driving force for a variable-pitch propeller, to be used on a future bomber, as eventually projected under the power plant designation 021. This was to give 3300hp at a speed of 900 km/h

(559 mph). In fact the S.11 was seen as an initial stage in the 021's development, but became the production type towards the end of the war. It appears that an enormous number of experimental and prototype S.11 engines were at one time ordered, but, after some of the second series of engines had been built, emphasis shifted to 109-011A-0 preproduction examples. By January 1945 four engines of the second series had accumulated a total of 184 hours of running.

By early 1942 Heinkel was progressing fairly well with the He 280, especially in view of Messerschmitt's inability to fly its Me 262 without the use of a piston engine in its nose. Of course this was not the fault of the airframe, but the non-availability of the Junkers Jumo 004 engine. Yet still positive steps were not being made by the RLM to progress towards He 280 production, although in 1941 six further prototypes had been ordered. A demonstration was considered the only way of really proving the He 280's ability as a fighter and so a mock dogfight was arranged between an He 280 and the best piston-engined fighter than available to the Luftwaffe, the Focke-Wulf Fw 190. In this the He 280 outflew the Fw 190; almost immediately thirteen preproduction He 280As were ordered.

The jubilation was short lived for Heinkel. As the S.8 engine was still not producing the required thrust, Heinkel reluctantly re-engined an He 280 with preproduction Junkers Jumo 004A turbojets. Therefore in July 1942 both the He 280 and Me 262 flew with 004A engines. Heavier than the S.8s, the 004As were nevertheless successful, but more so on the Me 262, as subsequent flights proved. In 1943 the S.8 engine was abandoned. Meanwhile the S.30 had been showing real promise. It first ran in October 1942 and was now the only Heinkel-Hirth engine that could be used in an early production He 280. However the RLM took a different view and ordered the S.30 to be abandoned also, in order to direct all energy to the S.11.

This decision has often been condemned by historians and indeed it did cause the premature end of a promising engine. But, seen from the RLM's point of view, the decision was not so wrong. By this time the ministry had the sound Junkers Jumo 004 as its first generation turbojet, which proved suitable for the He 280 and Me 262 prototypes, and saw the S.11 (109-011) as a follow-on type, with other engines in the pipeline.

Now that the two aircraft were flying with similar engines, the RLM could compare like with like. The Me 262 was not without its problems, but in most respects it appeared to hold greater promise. Above all, the Me 262 had a much better combat radius by virtue of its larger fuel tanks. Its cannon armament was also heavier than that originally proposed for the He 280. But still the final choice was not easy and it was complicated further when Heinkel suggested that an improved fighter-bomber version of its He 280, with more powerful Jumo 004B engines, would far outpace the 004A-engined aircraft then flying. As a fighter-bomber was close to the heart of the RLM, the proposal nearly won the day. But when further investigation showed that the Me 262 with 004B engines could prove even better, development of the He 280 was finally ordered to end in early 1943. The period of backing both 'horses' had ended. It is sometimes claimed that the personality tangle between members of the RLM and Ernst Heinkel had much to do with this decision, but it should be realized that the He 280 had other problems, including a very suspect tailplane. Therefore only the nine prototypes of the He 280 were built.

As mentioned earlier, Messerschmitt's Me 262 had to await delivery of the Jumo 004A engines before it could fly on turbojet power alone and indeed the first flight of an Me 262, on 18 April 1941, was on the power of a Junkers Jumo 210G piston engine installed in the nose. On 25 March 1942 the same aircraft, Me 262V1, took off under the power of the nose piston engine and two underwing BMW 003 turbojets, but the latter engines failed. Therefore it was not until 18 July 1942 that Me 262V3 flew with only the 004As. Well before the He 280 was abandoned officially, extra Me 262 prototypes and preproduction examples had been ordered. The latter were to use the improved 004B engine and in consequence it was not until October 1943 that the first appeared as Me 262V6.

So-called preproduction aircraft up to V12 were used in various tests, but Me 262s that were completed thereafter, up to the agreed total of 30 preproduction aircraft ordered, became true Me 262A-0s. Most of these were delivered from April 1944 to the specially-formed evaluation unit Erprobungskommando 262, which also later re-

ceived the first full production Me 262A-1a fighters. It was this unit that claimed the first Allied aircraft destroyed by jet aircraft, during a series of experimental interceptions, but the unit's main role was to formulate tactics and train pilots. Interceptions of a number of reconnaissance aircraft were made, but on 25 July an RAF Mosquito survived an Me 262 attack in which the jet was lost. By then production was gradually stepping up and just over a month later P-47 Thunderbolt fighters of the USAAF's 78th Fighter Group destroyed an Me 262A-2a fighter-bomber of KG 51 Kommando Schenk, which had moved to Juvincourt on 10 July to begin operations over France with just a handful of aircraft. But why was a fighter-bomber the first Me 262 brought down by US fighters and how did the jet rate against fully-developed piston-engined fighters of 1944?

As later experience showed, the Me 262 fighter was an outstanding warplane with

Below: the Heinkel He 162A-2 Volksjäger was intended to be a mass-produced home defense fighter.

much higher performance than any piston-engined fighter. It is for this reason that historians often write that had the fighter been ready for service earlier, and in greater numbers, it could have altered the course of the war. One often quoted reason for delay in getting numbers of jet fighters into operational use was Hitler's insistence that the Me 262 should be a fighter-bomber and not merely a cannon-armed fighter. This role had been ordered by Hitler in late 1943 and reaffirmed after the Allied in-vasion of Normandy on 6 June 1944. To say the least, Hitler was not pleased when informed that the Me 262A-0s and early production aircraft had no provision for carrying bombs. Me 262A-1a Schwalbe (Swallow) fighters on the production lines were ordered to be converted into Me 262A-2a Sturmvogel (Stormbird) fighter-bombers, with provision for two 250kg bombs or one 500kg bomb and associated equipment. It is probably true to say that Hitler had already accepted advice that some of the Me 262s being built ought to be fighters, but, on finding that none had been built as fighter-bombers, was furious. Although wishing to advise against this course, those around Hitler retreated and for a decisive period fighter-bombers were given priority.

The modification from fighter to fighter-bomber did not hold up Me 262 production to any extent, but naturally delayed the widespread deployment of the pure jet fighter. Only in November 1944 was the

emphasis on the fighter-bomber variant dropped, when all-out production of fighters was seen as the only way of curbing the crippling armadas of Allied bombers raiding Germany. Apart from lowering the Me 262's performance, because of the added weight of bombs, its adoption as a fighter-bomber was also responsible in part for a quirk of history, for no Allied jet fighter ever met a German jet in aerial combat, despite RAF Meteors being sent into Europe with the 2nd Tactical Air Force.

Whatever Hitler's policy toward the aircraft's role, the real reason for delay in getting substantial numbers of Me 262s into service was technical rather than political. Whilst airframes could be produced at a gradually increasing rate from early 1944, development of the turbojet had taken longer than expected. Indeed it was not until mid-year that the engine was considered suitably developed for mass production. Original Me 262 production schedules went out of the window, as did

later schedules that called for the production of more than 1300 by the end of 1944. For whatever reason, including Allied bombing raids on manufacturing plant, only 1433 Me 262s of all versions were built and just 200 or thereabouts became operational with the Luftwaffe. Versions of the aircraft produced, other than those already men-

Below: the de Havilland Vampire F. Mk. I was too late to see wartime service in 1945.

tioned, included the Me 262B-1a tandem two-seat trainer, Me 262B-1a/U1 and B-2a night fighters and the Me 262C rocket-assisted interceptor.

The Me 262 itself was powered by two 900kg (1984lb) thrust Junkers Jumo 004B eight-stage axial-flow turbojet engines in nacelles below the cantilever low and marginally-swept wings. Each engine was started by a Riedel two-stroke motor. The near triangular-section, semi-monocoque, all-metal fuselage was built in four parts and housed the four main fuel tanks with a total capacity of 2570 litres (566 Imperial gallons) of J-2 diesel oil fuel. The nose cone section incorporated four 30mm MK 108 cannon, two with 100 rounds of ammunition each and two with 80 rounds each. The pilot sat high in the cockpit under a sideways-hinged canopy, protected by 15mm armor plate and a 90mm bullet-resisting windscreen. Maximum speed for the fighter was an incredible 868 km/h (539 mph).

The controversy as to whether the Me 262 or Gloster Meteor was the first jet to enter operational service still goes on, although it is more generally accepted that the German aircraft beat the British type to this honor. It is certainly true that Erprobungskommando 262 flew Me 262s well before No 616 Squadron RAF received Meteor F.Mk Is, but this was not a fully operational unit in the accepted definition. Certainly other German units had Me 262s in July, but whether they became fully operational until August is another matter. Even General-leutnant Adolf Galland, who formed and led JV 44, has been said to have quoted August. What is known is that on 12 July 1944 No 616 Squadron received the first operational Meteors, each of which was powered by two 771kg (1700lb) thrust Rolls-Royce Welland I turbojet engines mounted within the cantilever low and tapering wings. In fact the engines were positioned near the extremities of the wing center-section, which was integral with the oval-section all-metal stressed-skin fuselage. Armament comprised four 20mm British Hispano cannon and a camera gun was installed in the nose. As with the Me 262, the pilot sat high in the cockpit, protected by armor plate and a bullet-resisting windscreen.

Britain had pulled out all the stops in getting the Meteor into service so quickly, especially bearing in mind that the Gloster E.28/39 had not flown by the time Heinkel was flying its He 280 prototype fighter. Helped by the use of eight F. 9/40 prototypes, with which to test various British engines, the development of the actual fighter was rapid. The first F.9/40 prototype flew for the first time on 5 March 1943 with Halford H.1 (Goblin) engines fitted, followed by the W2B-engined F.9/40 in June of that year. The Metropolitan-Vickers F.2/1-engined F.9/40 flew on 13 November 1943 (to become the first prototype flying with axial-flow turbojet engines), while the most unusual was undoubtedly the Rolls-Royce Trent-engined aircraft.

Meteor F.Mk Is were declared operational on 27 July and on that day began operations against V-1 flying-bombs, which had been directed at Britain since 13 June. An attempt to shoot down a V-1 on that day proved abortive, but on 4 August one was destroyed when the pilot of a Meteor flew alongside the missile and tipped it over with his aircraft's wing. On the same day another V-1 was brought down by cannon fire. The Meteor had arrived, albeit flying at only 676 km/h (420 mph).

Only twenty Meteor F.Mk Is were produced, most of which flew with No 616 Squadron. Of the remaining four, three were used as development aircraft and one was sent to America in exchange for a US-built Bell P-59 Airacomet. Other wartime Meteor variants included the prototype F.Mk 2 (with Goblin engines) and the F.Mk 3. The latter was the first major production version of the Meteor, of which all but 15 of the 280 built were powered by Derwent I engines. The F.Mk 3 had provision for a fuselage drop-tank to increase range. Maximum speed of this version was 793 km/h (493 mph). Later versions of the Meteor are covered in the next chapter.

Another British jet fighter which was built and flown during World War II was the de Havilland DH.100 Vampire. This was very different from the Meteor in that it was designed to use only one Goblin turbojet engine. Because of this, and in order not to lose any of the available 1225kg (2700lb) of thrust, the engine was placed in a short fuselage nacelle aft of the pilot's cockpit, which did away with the need for a long air intake and long jetpipe. This installation necessitated a twin-boom tail unit. In fact the fuselage nose was basically that from the company's highly-successful Mosquito and was, therefore, of plywood-balsa-plywood sandwich construction. The straight but tapering wings were all-metal and incorporated the engine air intakes in the roots. The prototype Vampire flew for the first time on 20 September 1943 and the first production aircraft flew on 20 April 1945. However Vampires did not enter service with the RAF until 1946.

Above: an American Bell P-59 Airacomet was exchanged for a British Gloster Meteor in 1943.

A single-engined jet fighter was also built in Germany, but under very different circumstances. By September 1944 the most Germany could hope to do was to defend itself against Allied forces closing in on all fronts. At the beginning of that month it was decided that, despite the production of the excellent Me 262, a new jet fighter was needed that could be produced quickly and in very great numbers to intercept Allied bombers that were destroying German factories and communications. This new fighter could be spared one engine only (a BMW 003), it had to be constructed of materials then available, it had to conform to strict weight and take off distance limitations but still achieve at least 750 km/h (466 mph), and could be armed with one or two 30mm cannon. Equally important was that it had to be simple enough to be built by

semi-skilled workers overseeing the un-skilled, thus making use of forced and voluntary labor.

Less than a week was allowed for initial proposals and several companies sub-mitted designs. Messerschmitt wanted nothing to do with such a scheme, which appeared to encroach upon its own Me 262, but Heinkel was anxious to submit a design, having been banned from further work on jet aircraft after its He 280 episode. In fact Heinkel had already worked on the idea of a 'lightweight' fighter, as the Spatz (Spar-row), and this formed the basis of the new Project 1073, which eventually became the He 162 Salamander.

Bearing in mind the necessity to keep the fighter simple, Heinkel decided to adopt the V-1 flying-bomb approach to power plant and placed the single engine on the top of the fuselage, exhausting through a V-tail. For the RLM, only two designs appeared to be worth pursuing seriously, those of Blohm und Voss and Heinkel, with a

strong bias for the former. But Heinkel kept up the pressure, pointing out that it had progressed further with development and was therefore in a better position to meet the tight schedules.

On 23 September the decision was made to go ahead with the concept of a Volks-jäger (People's Fighter) and the Heinkel proposal was selected, a decision helped by the display of a mock-up which had been completed by 20 September. The idea of a Volksjäger reflected Hitler's own thinking for the setting up of a vast Home Guard-type force to protect the homeland against the advancing Allies, with members of the Hitler Youth and old men making up short-ages in numbers. Independently Goering envisioned thousands of members of the Hitler Youth being trained to fly on gliders, the most promising then progressing on to the Volksjäger with little or no intermediate powered flight training. This vast intake of new pilots would match the massive pro-duction of jet fighters at conventional plant

and in the underground salt and potassium mine factories. Heinkel pulled out all the stops in order to meet schedules, but at least Ernst Heinkel knew full well that the whole concept of boy pilots was a pipedream and at best would provide only a respite from the inevitable defeat of Germany.

On 29 September Heinkel received the contract and on 6 December the prototype He 162 flew for the first time at Vienna-Schwechat, completing 20 minutes in the air. the elapsed time between contract and first flight had been just 69 days, 90 from the conception of the Volksjäger by the RLM. On 10 December a second flight ended in disaster, when the He 162 crashed after losing the leading-edge and tip of one wing and an aileron. The Volksjäger had claimed its first victim.

On examination it became clear that the design of the wooden wings with straight leading-edges and detachable metal tips was not the cause of the accident, but that the bonding used had caused some deterioration of the wood: the stress of a high speed dash had been too great for the deteriorated structure. However this is not to say that the He 162 was otherwise pleasant to fly. Far from it, as it proved relatively unstable because of the position of the engine and required careful use of the controls. It is interesting to note that the once-favored Blohm und Voss design had the engine more sensibly mounted inside the fuselage, exhausting below a 'boom' tail to avoid the loss of power which a long jetpipe would entail.

Although the Volksjäger was to be flown by pilots not already in the Luftwaffe, a Luftwaffe evaluation unit was set up to take the first production He 162s. Similarly it was later decided expedient to allow experienced Luftwaffe pilots to crew the first operational aircraft. But Heinkel's impressive start in keeping to schedules could not be sustained and, whilst 50 production He 162s were ordered for January 1945, followed by 100 for February, and then quickly building up to 1,000 per month, only a handful of production aircraft were available by the end of January. In the following month He 162s produced included prototypes for improved models.

Utter confusion followed, as production factories had to close with the Allied advance, including in April those in Vienna which had made use of voluntary non-German workers, while Luftwaffe units were moved from one airfield to another. On 3 May a number of He 162s were among the aircraft left behind by the retreating Germans at Salzburg, although they had been destroyed. On the following day I Einsatz-Gruppe JG 1 formed at Leck, mustering about fifty He 162s. This was the only He 162-equipped group at the end of the war and during its four days at Leck it only managed a minimum of flying, mainly because of fuel shortages. On 8 May the group surrendered to the Allies. So ended Goering's grand Volksjäger plan. It is believed that between 250 and 300 He 162s had been built by the time of the German capitulation, with hundreds more nearing completion. Of these the Luftwaffe received 116, but the fighter was rarely seen in the air by Allied aircrews. Nevertheless Heinkel had achieved the near impossible with the He 162, which could fly at 840 km/h (522 mph) on the power of its single BMW 003E

Right: two Bell YP-59A Airacomet service test aircraft fly in echelon formation.

Above: Japan's only wartime jet fighter was the Nakajima Kikka, seen displayed in a museum.

engine, could climb to 6000m (19,685ft) in a little over 6.5 minutes, and was armed with two 20mm MG 151 cannon with 120 rounds of ammunition per gun.

Across the Atlantic the jet fighter was also in its infancy. In September 1941 the Bell Aircraft Corporation was requested to design a jet fighter using the British Whittle-type engine, an early example of which was received by General Electric. A preliminary design was submitted in October the same year, which was approved. The aircraft was given the USAAF designation XP-59A, which was devised to maintain strict secrecy, as it implied a variant of the experimental XP-59 pusher-engined (piston) and twin-boom fighter. The XP-59A

was designed very much on the lines of Bell's P-39 Airacobra/P-63A Kingcobra piston-engined fighters, apart from the power plant and mid-wings. Of all-metal construction, the XP-59A, named Airacomet, was a single-seater armed with one 37mm cannon and three 0.50in machine-guns in its extreme nose. Bomb racks were positioned under each wing. The two General Electric Type 1-A engines were mounted in nacelles beneath the wing roots, exhausting to the rear of the wing trailing-edges. This arrangement kept the air intakes and jetpipes to short lengths.

The detail design of the XP-59A took about six months, when work on component parts began. In September 1942 the first prototype was shipped to the secret aircraft flight testing base at Muroc in California, where the engines were started for the first time. On the last day of September the XP-59A undertook taxiing trials, and the next

day made its first flight lasting half an hour. On 2 October two very successful flights were made, one reaching an altitude of 3050m (10,000ft). In total three prototypes were built.

Thirteen service evaluation YP-59As followed, these being delivered in 1943. Actual production began with twenty P-59As with 750kg (1650lb) thrust General Electric I-16 or J31-GE-3 turbojet engines, followed by thirty P-59Bs with 907kg (2000lb) thrust J31-GE-5 engines, which entered USAAF service from August 1944. These were the only production examples of the Airacomet built and were used mainly as jet fighter trainers. The P-59B had a maximum speed of 665 km/h (413 mph), less than that being achieved by the highly-developed piston-engined fighters then in service and the prototypes of the Fisher P-75A Eagle type then flying.

Far more important to the postwar USAF

was the jet fighter under development at Lockheed, which in first prototype form used British-designed engines. In June 1943 Lockheed was requested to design and build a new single-seat fighter, using a British de Havilland H.1 turbojet as the power plant, which arrived in America in the following month and was delivered to Wright Field. The first prototype was to be completed in just 180 days as the XP-80 Shooting Star, but Lockheed bettered this by having it airborne within 143 days, on 8 January 1944.

Unlike the other American jet, the British Meteor and the German Me 262, the XP-80 had its engine installed in the fuselage center-section. Air intakes were positioned in the fuselage sides, just forward of the wing roots. Already two other prototypes and 13 service evaluation aircraft had been ordered, but these had to be modified considerably when the Allis-Chalmers

Company was unable to mass produce the H.1 in America. In consequence it was not until mid-1944 that the next XP-80A prototype could fly, incorporating a more-powerful 1700kg (3750lb) thrust General Electric I-40 engine, which meant a longer fuselage, greater wing span, a redesigned vertical tail and a modified and strengthened landing gear.

The thirteen YP-80As were powered by General-Electric J33-GE-9 or -11 engines and had six 0.50in machine guns instead of the previous five. The YP-80As were delivered to the USAAF from October 1944 and two were despatched to Europe. The first true production model was the P-80A, deliveries to the USAAF beginning in December 1945 and therefore P-80As not becoming active during World War II. Previously Lockheed had made preparations for P-80A construction at four plants and the North American Kansas City plant

was also to be included. With the end of the war in Europe cutbacks were made and the North American contract was terminated.

Japan's jet-powered fighter, known as the Nakajima Kikka and flown only twice in prototype form during the last few days of war (for a total of only a few minutes), was based on the German Me 262. It was powered by two 475kg (1047lb) thrust Ne-20 axial-flow turbojet engines. Had the war continued into 1946, there can be little doubt that Japanese and American jet fighters would have met, as other prototype and preproduction Kikka jets were in the process of being built. Similarly British and German jets would have fought each other in the skies of Europe. But one thing was certain in 1945, the early jet fighters had such advantages over well-developed piston-engined warplanes that there could be no turning back and no postwar slump in aircraft production.

3: FAREWELL THE PISTON

With the defeat of Germany the Allies began collecting up the tons of documents relating to advanced military projects, a large proportion of which related to aviation. Plenty of prototype and production aircraft with little or no damage could also be examined, many finding their way into other countries. It soon became clear that Germany had already begun considering aircraft with delta, fully swept and variable-geometry wings, together with

Above: the S-92 fighter was a Messerschmitt Me 262 built in Czechoslovakia after World War II.

advanced propulsion systems such as ramjets.

Because of the very advanced nature of some German research, it is often overlooked that Britain had overcome its pathetically slow start in developing turbojet-powered aircraft, finishing the war with sound airframes and excellent turbojet engines. It is true that British jets of the war period were not the fastest, but they held plenty of promise for development. As a victor, Britain was able to continue work on its Meteor and Vampire, whilst the Me 262 and He 162 died. However the Me 262 was reprieved temporarily, when a small number were completed in Czechoslovakia as S-92 fighters and CS-92 fighter-bombers.

Below: the Gloster Meteor F. Mk. 8 was the major production version of Britain's first jet fighter.

The last 15 Gloster Meteor F.Mk 3s built had longer nacelles around the Derwent engines. This feature, together with Derwent 5 engines, reduced wing span to increase the aircraft's rate of roll, a pressurised cabin for the pilot and the provision for carrying bombs and rockets, became standard on the postwar Meteor F.Mk 4. The first F.Mk 4 flew in April 1945 and on 7 November that year an example set up the first official world speed record for aircraft since early 1939, achieving 975.67 km/h (606.25 mph) at Herne Bay, Kent. Over the next few years other fighter, fighter-reconnaissance, two-seat training, two-seat night fighter (the NF.Mk 11 becoming the RAF's first jet night fighter in 1951) and unarmed

Overleaf: the Lockheed T-33A was the training variant of the P-80 Shooting Star and saw widespread service.

high-altitude reconnaissance variants of the Meteor were produced, the F.Mk 8 fighter becoming the major production version. This was a longer-range development of the F.Mk 4, featuring a redesigned cockpit which included a pilot ejection seat. The latter, which ultimately saved the lives of many pilots, had been first tested in an earlier Meteor on 24 July 1946, when the first 'live' ejection was made at a speed of 515 km/h (320 mph). In total approximately 3550 Meteors of all versions were built in Britain, nearly one-third as F.Mk 8s. Eleven other countries eventually acquired Meteors. During the Korean War, the F.Mk 8 was the only British-designed jet fighter to be flown operationally, serving with the RAAF.

The other British wartime jet, the Vampire, was somewhat overshadowed by the Meteor, but it nevertheless has the distinction of remaining in service with one or two air forces in the early 1980s. The prototype Vampire exceeded 805 km/h (500 mph) in the spring of 1944 and in this respect bettered the Meteor and the Bell Airacomet.

The F.Mk 1 entered production soon after, with an order for 120 sub-contracted to the English Electric Company. Goblin 1 engines powered the first forty production aircraft, superseded by the 1406kg (3100lb) thrust Goblin 2. The first 50 had three-piece canopies and used drop tanks to increase range, but subsequent fighters featured pressurized cockpits with bubble canopies and had larger fuel tanks in the wings.

No 247 Squadron RAF became the first to operate the Vampire in mid-1946, soon joined by other regular and auxiliary squadrons. A de Havilland Ghost-powered Vampire and the experimental Vampire Mk 2s with Rolls-Royce Nene 1 engines were fol-

lowed by the Goblin 2 engined Vampire F.Mk 3, a long-range fighter with increased fuel tankage and redesigned tail unit. The first F.Mk 3 flew on 4 November 1946. Six F.Mk 3s became the first RAF turbojet-powered aircraft to cross the North Atlantic in 1948.

In addition to RAF production, Vampire F.Mk 1s and F.Mk 3s were exported, the fighters having been ordered by Sweden, Switzerland, Norway and Canada. The Mk 4, the intended production version of the Mk 2, did not enter production in Britain, but was built under licence in Australia with Mk 30 series designations. Subsequent overseas versions included the FB.Mk 6 fighter-bomber powered by the 1500kg (3300lb) thrust Goblin 3 exported to, and built in, Switzerland, the similar Swedish FB.Mk 50, Norwegian FB.Mk 52 and the French FB.Mk 53. The latter is of particular interest as it was based on the FB.Mk 5 but entered production in France as the SNCASE Mistral. Powered by an Hispano-Suiza-built Nene engine, it was built entirely of French materials and followed French production of the FB.Mk 5. The first SNCASE-produced Vampire FB.Mk 5 flew on 27 January 1950 and SNCASE built 430 Vampire and Mistral aircraft in total.

The FB.Mk 5 itself was produced as a ground attack fighter for the RAF, using the Goblin 2 engine. Wing span was reduced from 12.19m (40ft) to 11.58m (38ft) and other changes included strengthened wings to allow for the provision of eight rockets and two 500lb bombs, two 1000lb bombs or two drop tanks. The first FB.Mk 5 flew in June

Left: this Shooting Star was one of a number of P-80As converted to carry cameras in the nose as FP-80As.

Below: the British D.H. Vampire was built under license in France as the SNCASE Mistral.

1948 and superseded the F.Mk 3, operating in Britain, Germany and the Middle and Far East. A special version of the FB.Mk 5 was produced for RAF squadrons operating in tropical climates as the FB.Mk 9. Other Vampires to enter production included two-seat trainers, the D.H.113 night fighter (95 two-seaters were flown by the RAF as NF.Mk 10s between 1951 and 1954) and the Sea Vampire. The prototype Sea Vampire was in fact a converted RAF fighter with an arrester hook and larger-area dive-brakes and landing flaps. On 3 December 1945 it landed and took off again from HMS *Ocean*, the first time a turbojet-powered aircraft performed this. The Navy received a small number of production Sea Vampires as F.Mk 20s, incorporating FB.Mk 5-type wings, although strengthened, and armed with the usual four 20mm British Hispano cannon. Including the very large number of trainers built, well over 2000 Vampires left production lines in Britain.

Between the end of the war and June 1947 the British Meteor F.Mk 4 held on to the world speed record for aeroplanes, increasing the record over that period. Then on 19 June a Lockheed Shooting Star achieved 1003.6 km/h (623.61 mph) at Muroc, California, bettering an unofficial Meteor speed set in September 1946 by a fraction of a second. This marked not only the beginning of America's dominance of the record, until the introduction of the British Hunter fighter, but the growing importance of the Shooting Star in USAAF service.

The P-80A went into service from December 1945, powered by one Allison

J33-A-9, -11 or -17 engine. Although it had been planned to produce 5000 of these fighters, postwar cancellations meant that only just over ten percent was actually built. These subsequently became F-80As under the new designation system. By March 1948 F-80As had ben modified to include water/alcohol injection, cockpit cooling, underwing rocket launchers and provision for JATO, features designed into the P-80B/F-80B, which also had a thinner wing, strengthened bulkheads in the nose, enclosed radio mast and antennae wires and a 2360kg (5200lb) thrust Allison J33-A-21 engine. Altogether 240 'Bs' were produced.

The final production version of the Shooting Star single-seat fighter was the P-80C/F-80C, powered by the 2360kg (5200lb) thrust J33-A-23 or 2450kg (5400lb) thrust J33-A-35 engine. Armament was improved by the use of six updated and faster-firing M-3 0.50in guns, as well as by the provision for carrying two 1000lb bombs or rockets. As with earlier versions, the guns and ammunition magazines could be replaced in fifteen minutes. A total of 798 P-80C/F-80Cs was built, one of which made history by shooting down a Chinese-flown Mikoyan-Gurevich MiG-15 over Korea on 8 November 1950, the first recorded victory of one jet fighter over another in combat. During this war the Shooting Star was operated mainly in a ground atack role. Thousands of sorties by Shooting Stars were made over Korea, although as a fighter it had to bow to the superior swept-wing North American F-86 Sabre. Non-combat versions of the Shooting Star included the RF-80C photographic reconnaissance aircraft, the T-33A two-seat trainer and the US Navy TO-1 and TO-2 (later TV-1 and 2) single and two-seat trainers and the T2V Seastar Navy trainer. It is worth noting that the T-33A became the most produced version, with well over 5000 being built.

Another combat aircraft, related to the T-33A, was the Lockheed F-94A Starfire. Powered by the Allison J33-A-33 turbojet, it was evolved as an all-weather fighter, with radar equipment in the nose. A radar operator occupied the rear tandem seat. Armed with four 0.50in guns, it used the wings, center fuselage and other components of the T-33A. One hundred and ten F-94As were produced, entering service with the USAF in mid-1950. The F-94A was followed by the refined F-94B, of which 357 were built. The most noticeable external change was its new wingtip tanks, positioned at the tips (not underneath as on the F-94A).

The final production version of the Starfire was the F-94C, powered by the 3765kg (8300lb) thrust Pratt & whitney J48-P-5 engine and incorporating a longer forward fuselage, thinner wings, new and swept horizontal tail surfaces, a larger fin and rudder and new main armament of 24 Mighty Mouse air-to-air rockets carried around the radome at the nose and covered by a circular retractable fairing. A similar number of rockets could be carried in a further two pods mounted on the wing leading edges. Production of the F-94C amounted to 387 aircraft.

When the Starfire entered service it became the USAF's first all-weather interceptor, beating the Northrop Scorpion, serving mainly with Air Defense Command. A single-seat tactical fighter version of the F-94C was proposed as the F-94D, for operation in Korea, but this idea went no further. It is interesting to note that despite its much heavier take-off weight, the F-94C's speed of 941 km/h (585 mph) was slightly higher than that of the F-80C.

Three other straight-winged American jet fighters appeared in production form soon after the end of World War II, namely the McDonnell FD-1 Phantom, the Republic F-84 Thunderjet and the Northrop F-89 Scorpion. The Phantom was in fact a naval fighter that had the distinction of being the first US fighter with turbojet power only to land on an aircraft carrier.

The Republic F-84 Thunderjet was the first of the other two to enter production for the USAAF, having flown in prototype form on 28 February 1946. As originally conceived, it was not only intended as a re-

placement for the piston-engined Republic P-47 Thunderbolt, but to be basically a redesign of it to take a General Electric TG-180 (J35) axial-flow turbojet engine. However in late 1944 this proposal was discarded in favor of producing a completely new airframe.

The Thunderjet became an all-metal aircraft with a circular-section fuselage of greatly varying diameter. The engine was placed inside the fuselage to the rear of the wings, the fuselage itself reducing in diameter towards the nose air intake and tail jetpipe. Because the rear section of the fuselage was detachable, the engine could be replaced in under an hour. Fuel tanks were in the wings, while jettisonable tip-tanks allowed for increased range. Armament comprised six 0.50in guns (four in the nose and two in the wings). From the 86th aircraft armament was increased by the use of retractable launchers beneath the wings for eight 5 inch rockets, although previous F-84Bs could carry rockets beneath the wings.

Above left: the Republic F-84E Thunderjet was operated as a fighter-bomber by the USAF.

Above: the Lockheed F-94C Starfire carried 24 Mighty Mouse rockets around the nose radome.

In September 1946 the second prototype Thunderjet attained a speed of 983 km/h (611 mph), thus setting a new American speed record. The usual batch of pre-production aircraft, in this case designated YF-84As and powered by 1814kg (4000lb) thrust Allison J35-A-15 engines, was followed by the full production F-84B (originally P-84B), deliveries of which began in 1947 to the 14th Fighter Group. The 'B' was powered by the similarly-rated J35-A-15C and the preproduction aircraft were brought up to this standard.

The F-84C was basically a slightly refined version of the 'B,' but the follow-on F-84D introduced many changes. Apart from being powered by the 2268kg (5000lb)

Above: an underside view of the Republic F-84F Thunderstreak prototype aircraft.

thrust Allison J35-A-17D turbojet, with a winterized fuel system using gasoline, it used thicker metal skins on the wings and ailerons, had a shorter landing gear with mechanical linkages and other changes. This version was the first to be flown in Korea, becoming active from the end of 1950.

From the F-84D was developed the F-84E, which had a longer fuselage to permit more room in the cockpit (increasing pilot comfort and efficiency); wingtip tanks fitted with fins to provide better maneuverability with the tanks attached (making it unnecessary to jettison the tanks before combat); structural changes to permit higher G forces; use of a radar gunsight; addition of two 230 US gallon (871 liter) drop tanks that could be carried by the inboard bomb shackles to increase the aircraft's radius of combat to more than 1609km (1000 miles), from the normal 1127km (700 miles) or thereabouts; provision for JATO (jet assisted take off) and other improvements. Armament also received attention, allowing for the carriage of 32 5in rockets (24 under the outer wings and eight on inboard stations), or two 1000lb bombs and 18 rockets. This armament indicated the Thunderjet's increasing importance as a fighter-bomber.

The F-84F was not the next version of the Thunderjet, but a more modern development of it named Thunderstreak. It was basically a swept-wing F-84E, powered by a 3275kg (7220lb) thrust Armstrong Siddeley Sapphire ASSa 3 turbojet engine which was being produced in the United States under license by the Wright Aeronautical Corporation. Interestingly the Sapphire was a development of the original

Metropolitan Vickers engine. The prototype Thunderstreak, powered by an Allison J35-A-25 engine, took off for the first time on 3 June 1950 as the YF-96A, but the second prototype flew on 14 February 1951 with the Sapphire engine as the XF-84F. The production F-84F became operational with the USAF in 1954, but approximately half of the

2711 aircraft built were acquired by other NATO air forces. Maximum level speed of the F-84F was 1058 km/h (658 mph), compared to the F-84E's 986 km/h (613 mph). A tactical reconnaissance version of the Thunderstreak was the RF-84F Thunderflash, which could be identified easily by the fairing-over of the nose air intake (replaced by intakes in the wing roots) to provide accommodation for the cameras, radar and other electronic equipment. By the end of 1956 a total of 715 Thunderflash reconnaissance aircraft had been built.

Like the later Thunderstreak, F-84E Thunderjets were also acquired by other NATO air forces. However by far the most important version of the Thunderjet was the F-84G, which became the first fighter-bomber operated by the USAF to be capable of carrying and delivering an atomic bomb. It was powered by the 2540kg (5600lb) thrust Allison J35-A-29 turbojet engine, was capable of inflight refuelling using the 'flying boom' method, had an automatic pilot fitted and proved to be the

Above: the F-84G Thunderjet was supplied to many NATO air forces, including that of Turkey.

Left: a pair of Northrop F-89 Scorpion all-weather interceptor fighters fly in formation during 1956.

fastest version of the Thunderjet with a maximum level speed of 1001 km/h (622 mph). Of the 4457 Thunderjets of all versions built, the 'G' amounted to 3025, deliveries to other NATO air forces and others eligible under MAP (Military Assistance Program) accounting for 1936.

The Northrop F-89 Scorpion was evolved as a two-seat, all-weather jet interceptor fighter and in this respect was similar to the Lockheed Starfire. However although its development had begun as early as 1946, it followed the Starfire into USAF service, not becoming operational until 1951. The XF-89 prototype first flew on 16 August 1948 and during the course of its test program the ailerons were replaced by 'decelerons,' new power-operated ailerons which were split to serve as both ailerons and dive brakes. As dive brakes, the upper and lower segments could be extended up and down simultaneously. Power was provided by two 1814kg (4000lb) thrust Allison J35-A-9 engines, mounted one each side of the fuselage under the wings, partly submerged into the fuselage contours.

The second prototype was powered by

2222kg (4900lb) thrust J35-A-21 engines with afterburners and was followed by the first 18 production Scorpions designated F-89As. Armament comprised six 20mm cannon in the nose and the J35-A-21 engines were later replaced by more powerful J35-A-21As. The second production version was also produced in small numbers, differing little from the F-89A. The first major production version was the F-89C, which was fitted during its production run with several different engines up to the J35-A-33A. Like previous Scorpions, it too had wingtip fuel tanks (fitted with horizontal fins) and could supplement its gun armament with bombs and a small number of rockets. Its main innovation was the use of new internally-balanced elevators, which were subsequently fitted to earlier aircraft in place of the previously-used external mass balances.

Of the 1050 Scorpions built, more than 680 were F-89Ds. The majority were powered by 2540kg (5600lb) thrust J35-A-35 engines. The 'D' was the first and only version of the Scorpion to use the newly-developed wing-tip pods, each containing fuel and 52 2.75in folding-fin air-to-air rockets, the gun armament being deleted. Rockets could be fired in batches of seven or in a volley from behind fairings. Other important changes included the use of two jettisonable under-wing pylon-mounted auxiliary fuel tanks for extended range.

The experimental XF-89E (Allison J71 engines), F-89F and F-89G remained prototypes and projects, leaving the F-89H as the follow-on to the F-89D. In this version new wingtip pods each carried 21 rockets and three Hughes Falcon air-to-air missiles, the latter emerging from the pods before firing. Underwing pylons allowed a further batch of Falcon missiles to be carried. F-89Hs became operational in 1956, three years after the 'D,' but served for only a very short time with Air Defense Command. However a further version of the Scorpion appeared as the F-89J, basically an F-89D modified to carry two Douglas MB-1 Genie air-to-air missiles with nuclear warheads, as well as four Falcon missiles and rockets.

In Europe both France and Sweden got off to an early start by producing jet fighters in the 1940s. Sweden had been among the few countries experimenting with a turbojet engine prior to the outbreak of World War II and on 10 March 1947 Saab flew a version of its Model 21A pusher-engined fighter with the DB 605B piston engine replaced by a Goblin turbojet. In this configuration the aircraft became the Saab-21R. The Flygvap-

net (Swedish air force) received sixty aircraft from 1950, powered by Goblin 2 and SFA-built Goblin 3 engines with the military designations J21RA and J21RB respectively. As a fighter the Saab-21R was armed with one 20mm cannon and two 13mm Bofors guns in the nose and two guns in the wings, as was standard for the piston-engined version. A pack containing eight guns could also be carried under the fuselage nacelle. However because of the rapid development of the purpose-designed Saab-29, the Saab-21R soon found itself transferred to a ground attack role as the A 21R.

The Saab-29 was the first purpose-designed Swedish jet fighter, originally intended to have straight wings but later revised to become in production form the first European fully swept-wing fighter. The Saab-29 joined the F13 day fighter wing of the Flygvapnet at Norrköping in 1951. Three prototypes were ordered, the first of which flew initially on 1 September 1948 on the power of a de Havilland Ghost engine, rated at 1996kg (4400lb) thrust. Because of its unique shape, the aircraft soon received the popular name Tunnan (barrel). All production Saab-29s were powered by SFA

license-built Ghost 50 engines, known to the air force as the RM2 and rated at 2268kg (5000lb) thrust. The final version (military designation J 29F) used a Swedish-developed afterburner to raise thrust to 2800kg (6170lb), in this form the engine receiving the revised designation RM2B. The Ghost was installed inside a dumpy fuselage and exhausted beneath the tail unit. Such was the size of the fuselage, it was able to house the short landing gear when retracted, the fuel tanks, the four 20mm cannon armament and other equipment.

The initial production version of the Saab-29 was the J 29A, deliveries starting in May 1951. Initially the air brakes were wing mounted, but these later gave way to others on the fuselage. In 1953 the 'A' was superseded on the production lines by the J 29B, which had greater range by virtue of increased fuel capacity. An attack version of this model also appeared as the A 29B. The 'C' designation applied only to the S 29C photographic reconnaissance aircraft, also delivered in 1953, which carried six fully-automatic cameras.

In March 1954 the J 29D flew, but it remained an experimental version, being used to flight test the afterburner developed by SFA and the Swedish Air Board. Meanwhile in December 1953 a new outer wing had been flight tested which had been designed to increase maximum speed and improve the aircraft's flying characteristics at transonic speed. This was incorporated into production aircraft the following year, thus producing the J 29E fighter.

The final production versions of the Saab-29 were the J 29F fighter and A 29F attack aircraft, which were basically 'Es' fitted with the newly-developed afterburner. The pre-production J 29F had been flown in the first half of 1954 and deliveries of production aircraft were made between late 1954 and April 1956. The 'F' attained a maximum level speed of 1060 km/h (659 mph). In total 661 Saab-29s were built, and although several hundred earlier models were thereafter gradually brought up to 'F' standard, by 1956 Saab had already begun delivery of its latest Model 32 Lansen, and had flown a research aircraft (known as the Saab-210 Draken) which helped to develop the Saab-35 Draken fighter.

Because of the German occupation during the first half of the 1940s, France took longer to get a jet fighter into service than would otherwise have been the case. Nevertheless, its first production jet fighter, the Dassault M.D.450 Ouragan (Hurricane), was designed and constructed in a very short time. Despite the occupation, work on a turbojet-powered aircraft began as early as 1943. Although it was possible to carry out theoretical and design work in secrecy, actual construction of an airframe could not begin until after liberation. It was therefore in 1945 that the construction of five prototype Sud-Ouest SO 6000 Triton experimental two-seat jet trainers was ordered, the first to be powered by one German Junkers Jumo 004B turbojet and the rest by Hispano-Suiza-built Nene 101 engines. On 11 November 1946 the Jumo-powered SO 6000 took to the air for the first time. France had joined the exclusive few countries flying jets. A Nene-powered SO 6000 followed on 19 March 1948.

While France waited for its own aircraft industry to produce a jet fighter, it filled the time-gap by accepting British Vampires into service. The problem France might have experienced in developing rapidly its own turbojet engine was also removed by the production of the Nene engine by

Left: an F-89D Scorpion fires its wingtip rockets. A total of 104 air-to-air rockets was carried.

Above: the Saab-21R jet fighter was a
development of the earlier Model 21A
piston-engined aircraft.

Hispano-Suiza. It was around this engine that a specification was issued and in December 1947 Avions Marcel Dassault began work on what became the Ouragan. An official order was given for three prototypes on 1 July 1948, by which time construction at the Dassault plant had already begun. The first prototype made its maiden flight on 29 February 1949.

The Ouragan itself was a fine design, using low-mounted wings with symmetrical laminar-flow section. Leading-edges were swept at 20 degrees and trailing-edges were straight. The circular-section fuselage was built in three sections, the nose section containing the frontal air intake, pilot's cockpit and nose wheel, the center section carried the engine, fuel tanks and radio equipment; the engine exhausting at the tail. Fuel tanks were also carried in the wings,

outboard of the landing gear, while wingtip tanks allowed extended range. Armament comprised four 20mm cannon, plus optionally 16 rockets carried under the wings. Naturally, the Ouragan was the first French jet fitted with an ejection seat, produced by Martin-Baker.

Trials with the prototype Ouragans were so successful that no time was lost in ordering preproduction fighters, the first of which flew in November 1950. Full production then went ahead and in December 1951 the initial Ouragans for the French air force flew. Altogether the air force received 350, production of 30 each month being achieved by the beginning of 1953. About one-third of the production was sub-contracted to SNCASO and SNCASE. The Ouragan was also exported to India (renamed Toofani) and Israel, although most of the eventual Israeli

total of more than 50 were ex-French air force fighters. Maximum level speed of the Ouragan was 940 km/h (584 mph).

It is not overstating the case to say that British-developed turbojet engines were fundamental in getting most of the world's earliest jet fighters into the air. America had used British engines during World War II for its Bell Airacomet and Lockheed Shooting Star prototypes and after the war, France and Sweden had used British turbojets. Other nations were to follow this lead. Likewise it was only after Britain had delivered 25 Rolls-Royce Nene and 30 Derwent engines to the Soviet Union in 1947 that Soviet jet fighter design really took off in a big way. Many have since stated that this one act gave the Soviet Union such a boost that it was responsible for undermining the lead built up in the West, allowing that

nation to bypass lengthy development of its own engines, or those captured from the Germans. Although there can be little doubt that the Rolls-Royce engines were of great value in this respect, the Soviet Union had managed to get a small number of very respectable jet fighters into service on the power of German-type engines alone. Also the great importance attached to the development of jet fighters by the Soviet Union in 1945 would have ensured rapid development with or without outside help.

During World War II the Soviet Union had had to put the bulk of its energy into the production of conventional weapons with which to drive German forces from its land. Often updates and modifications to improve aircraft were introduced without break in production and it was partly because of this that the only non-conventional form of pro-

pulsion used on aircraft was the rocket motor. Even then it was seen as a 'booster' and not as the main form of power as used by the Germans towards the end of the war.

The Soviet Union saw the need for both twin-jet and single-engined fighters to replace wartime piston aircraft and therefore issued two initial specifications. Interestingly the two most successful jet fighters, one single-engined and the other twin, both flew for the first time on the same day. For the twin-engined competition, Mikoyan-Gurevich produced its I-300, an impressive aircraft with straight wings. The circular-section fuselage had a divided nose air intake, which fed two developed 800kg (1764lb) thrust German BMW 003A turbojet engines mounted side by side in the rear fuselage and exhausting under the tail. This flew for the first time on 24 April 1946. In

competition was a Sukhoi jet, first flown in August that year. This used two Junkers Jumo 004B engines in pods under the wings and looked remarkably like a straight-winged Messerschmitt Me 262. The Sukhoi was not well received and indeed had a maximum speed very similar to the wartime Me 262. It was the I-300 that was selected for production as the MiG-9, its designers receiving a Stalin Prize.

The production MiG-9 used two RD-20 turbojet engines, the Soviet development and production model of the BMW, and armament comprised one 37mm Nudelmann N-37 cannon projecting from the nose and two 23mm NS-23 cannon under the

Below: the final version of the Saab J 29 Tunnan was the J 29F, which used afterburning.

Left: the Yak-23 served in small numbers with Soviet satellite air forces, a Polish fighter is shown.

nose. With a maximum speed of 910 km/h (565 mph), the MiG-9 entered service with the air force, but was not its first jet fighter. It remained operational until the early 1950s, when the fighter received the NATO reporting name *Fargo*. In addition to being based in the Soviet Union, a number were to be found in East Germany. Developments included a version with RD-21 engines.

For the single-engined jet fighter competition Lavochkin produced its La-150 and Yakovlev an adaption of the piston-engined Yak-3 which later became the Yak-15. As with all of the first Soviet jet fighter prototypes except for the Sukhoi, the La-150 used an engine which exhausted under the rear fuselage and tail. Power was provided by the RD-10, the Soviet developed version of

the German Junkers Jumo 004B. Although more work had probably gone into the development of this prototype than the Yak-15, the Lavochkin was not selected. However in 1947 Lavochkin produced its La-160, the first Soviet jet fighter prototype with swept wings. It was followed by the La-168, which subsequently lost a competition against the MiG-15 as a second-generation fighter, and the La-174, which in 1949 joined the air force in limited numbers as a fighter-bomber, powered by a development of the Rolls-Royce Derwent engine (known as the RD-500). Capable of more than 1000 km/h (620 mph), the La-174 received the military designation La-15 in production form and the reporting name *Fantail* by NATO.

The winner of the lightweight jet fighter competition, the Yak-15, first flew in prototype form on 24 April 1946. It was basically a

Yak-3 with the piston engine removed and an RD-10 installed in the forward fuselage. Air for the engine passed through a nose intake and the engine exhausted below the cut-away rear fuselage virtually below the pilot's cockpit. To ensure that no damage was caused to the rear fuselage from the running engine, the underside was covered by heat-resistant metal. Two 23mm NS-23 cannon provided nose armament. During trials it is said that Olga Yamschikova, a company employee, flew the aircraft, which would have made her the first woman in the world to fly a jet fighter.

In 1947 the Yak-15 entered service with the IA-PVO, to become the first jet fighter operated by the Soviet air forces. It is believed to have had a maximum speed of 786 km/h (488 mph), although some reports suggested a figure slightly over 805 km/h (500 mph). From the start the Yak-3-type tailwheel landing gear had given trouble, even though the tailwheel itself was all-metal and for this reason it was subsequently decided to adapt the Yak-15 to

have a nosewheel gear. A similar landing gear was used on the follow-on Yak-17, basically an improved Yak-15 powered by the developed 1000kg (2204lb) thrust RD-10A turbojet. A tandem two-seat version, known as the Yak-17UTI, became the first Soviet jet trainer. The Yak-17 remained operational long enough to receive the NATO reporting name *Feather* and possessed a maximum speed of 830 km/h (515.5 mph). Including two-seaters, 430 Yak-17s were built, a few going to Czechoslovakia and Poland. It is of interest to note that the Yak-16 was not a fighter but a ten-passenger transport aircraft with piston engines.

In order to obtain the best possible results from the basic Yak-15/17 shape and yet to compete with more radical fighter prototypes being designed to use the Soviet-built versions of the British Nene and Derwent engines, Yakovlev produced its Yak-23. This can be viewed as the definative development of the first generation fighter. As well as being of all-metal con-

struction, the Yak-23 airframe was virtually completely revised, the most obvious external change being the mid-mounted tailplane. As with the Yak-17, wingtip fuel tanks helped to increase range. Power was provided by the RD-500, the 1600kg (3525lb) thrust Soviet development of the Derwent turbojet. Although considerably heavier than the previous Yak jets, the extra power of the RD-500 allowed a maximum speed of more than 965 km/h (600 mph). Remarkably armament remained light. More than 300 Yak-23s were produced, entering service with the air force in 1948 and later being acquired in small numbers by Czechoslovakia, Poland and other eastern bloc nations. However development of the MiG-15 curtailed the Yak-23's operational life in the Soviet Union, although it received the NATO reporting name *Flora*.

Among the last straight-winged jet

Below: the Avro CF-100 first flew in 1950 and the last examples remained in Canadian service until the 1980s.

fighters built was the Canadian Avro CF-100, which like so many other jet fighters began life on the power of a British engine. Design of the CF-100 began as early as 1946, but it was not until January 1950 that the first prototype took off for a flight, powered by two Rolls-Royce Avon turbojet engines mounted one each side of the fuselage at the wing roots. The two prototypes were known as Mk 1s, and were the only CF-100s so powered. Orenda Engines Ltd had formed out of the old A. V. Roe Canada gas turbine division, and in February 1949 first ran the prototype Orenda 1 axial-flow turbojet engine, two and a half years after design work had begun. An Orenda (a modified Orenda 1 known as the Orenda 3) was first flight tested on a North American F-86A Sabre in October 1950. The Orenda engine was then put into production as the Orenda 2. This engine had been developed specifically for the CF-100 and on 20 June 1951 the first preproduction Mk 2 fighter flew with Orenda 2s. The 2882kg (6355lb) thrust Orenda 9 was chosen as the power plant for the production CF-100 Mk 3, as it was suitable for installation in either left or right hand engine nacelles. First flown in October 1952, the CF-100 Mk 3, armed with eight 0.50in Colt-Browning machine-guns carried in a replaceable ventral tray, entered RCAF service in 1953. Altogether seventy Mk 3s were built, 50 later being converted into dual-control trainers.

When Mk 3s first entered service, they were the RCAF's first all-weather fighters and the first and only production jet fighters of indigenous design and manufacture. In total 692 CF-100s were built in various models, including prototypes. Among these were 3300kg (7275lb) thrust Orenda 11-powered CF-100 Mk 4Bs, armed with 48 2.75in air-to-air rockets, and similarly-powered CF-100 Mk 5s of 1955, with 52 rockets in each wingtip pod (Scorpion fashion). Fifty-three ex-RCAF CF-100 Mk 5s also served with the Belgian Air Force. Maximum speed of the CF-100 Mk 4B and Mk 5 was 1046 km/h (650 mph), the fighter having already become the first straight-winged jet fighter to exceed the speed of sound (on 18 December 1952). Although re-tired as combat aircraft in 1963, Canadian CF-100s continued flying into the 1980s, when a few Mk 5s were still listed as being used by the Canadian Armed Forces for utility and electronic countermeasures training roles. However by 1981 these had been retired.

Similar longevity has befallen the Soviet-designed Mikoyan-Gurevich MiG-15 and

the US-designed North American F-86 Sabre, which can be regarded as the first of the second-generation jet fighters. The earlier described Saab-29 can also be termed 'second generation.' In the early 1980s MiG-15bis and MiG-15UTIs are still being operated as trainers, while the last few Sabres retain some measure of attack capability. Chapter Six covers the bulk of the jet fighters built and flown in the 1950s, so why mention them here? Incredible as it might seem, the prototypes of the MiG-15

and Sabre first flew on 30 December 1947 and 1 October 1947 respectively, production aircraft of each type entering service in 1948 and 1949.

The Sabre became the USAF's first swept-wing fighter, and one of aviation history's all-time greats. But, in a classic 'chicken or egg' situation, it is a common misconception to believe that its naval counterpart, the FJ-2 Fury, was merely a derivative. The truth is far from this. Way back in 1944 North America had produced

the design of a straight-winged naval jet fighter, which eventually became the FJ-1 Fury, first flying in 1946. A USAAF derivative subsequently received the designation XP-86, but was known first by the company number N.A.140. This too had straight wings. Three prototypes were ordered as the war in Europe ended, two as flying prototypes. However material confiscated in Germany revealed many advanced aviation projects, including the use of swept wings, and before the end of the year the XP-86 had

been redesigned with swept wings and swept tail surfaces.

The two flying XP-86s were each engined by one 1700kg (3750lb) thrust Allison J35-C-3 turbojet mounted inside the oval-section fuselage, with a nose intake feeding air direct to the engine. The main fuel tanks were also located in the fuselage. The first flew on 1 October 1947. Both were later reengined with General Electric J47s, as selected for the first production model of the fighter. It was on the power of this

Above: the USAF's North American F-86A Sabre was blooded in combat with the MiG-15 over Korea.

engine that one XP-86 exceeded the speed of sound on 25 April 1948. To get this achievement into perspective, the world's first aircraft to fly faster than the speed of sound had only achieved this on 14 October 1947 and this aircraft was the purely experimental and rocket-powered Bell X-1.

The initial Sabre production version was

Above: the F-86D was the first all-weather fighter version of the Sabre, with a nose-mounted APG-37 radar.

Below: the F-86K was an all-weather fighter supplied to NATO allies. A Norwegian F-86K is pictured.

the P-86A, soon after its appearance receiving the new USAF designation F-86A. The first of more than 550 F-86As flew in May 1948, the 1st Fighter Group receiving Sabres from February of the following year. F-86As were powered successively by J47-GE-1, -3, -7, -9 and -13 engines, rated at 2360kg (5200lb) thrust. Armament comprised six 0.50in machine-guns in the nose, while provision was made for sixteen 5in rockets or jettisonable drop tanks under the wings.

On 15 September 1948 an F-86A broke the existing world speed record, held by the Douglas Skystreak, by achieving slightly over 1079 km/h (670 mph). Sabres of the later 'D' version held the record until September 1953, when the British Hawker Hunter achieved 1170 km/h (727 mph).The 'A' went out of production in December

1950, but not before two had been made readily available to the Central Fighter Establishment of the RAF. Another F-86A was fitted and flown in America with a Canadian Orenda engine as part of that engine's development program.

There were no F-86Bs or F-86Cs as such, and the 'A' was followed on the production line at Los Angeles by the F-86E day fighter. Powered by J47-GE-13 engines, F-86Es differed from the previous model in having a 'flying tail,' in which the elevators and tailplane were designed to move differentially in coordination to allow in-flight trim, but in most other respects they were similar. United States production amounted to well over 300 aircraft.

Of the thousands of Sabres eventually built, the two main versions were the F-86D and F-86F. The former was the first all-

weather version, powered first by a J47-GE-17 engine and, on the last aircraft, by a 3470kg (7650lb) thrust J47-GE-33 engine, both types fitted with afterburners. The prototype F-86D flew for the first time on 22 December 1949 and the first production aircraft in March 1951. Apart from the change of engine, the F-86D introduced an undernose air intake, allowing for a new rounded nose containing the APG-37 radar scanner for all-weather operation. Naturally the F-86D was longer than previous versions

because of the new nose and armament also changed from guns to 24 Mighty Mouse air-to-air rockets carried in a retractable ventral tray. The last of just over 2500 'Ds' were delivered in September 1955, numbers going to other nations under MDAP (Mutual Defense Assistance Program).

The F-86F was even more numerous (just) and was a day fighter powered by the 2708kg (5970lb) thrust J47-GE-27. The first production 'F' flew in March 1952. Similar to the 'E' in many ways, this model introduced the so-called '6-3' wing, in which the leading-edges were of increased chord and small fences were fitted. This refinement and others gave the Sabre increased maneuverability at high altitude, an area in which the Soviet-built MiG-15s seemed to

excel during the Korean War, although at the expense of landing speed. The fallacy that Sabres were greatly superior to MiG-15s was partly caused by the 'F's' improved high-altitude performance and the Sabre's general availability.

In truth the MiG had a tighter turning circle at high altitude and better rate of climb, although it suffered stability and handling problems. It was the better trained pilots of the USAF that made the difference in Korea, although this does not reduce the credit due to the Sabre, which was in all respects an excellent fighter. The first pilot of a jet fighter to achieve five 'jet kills' and so become a 'jet ace' was Captain James Jabara of the 4th Fighter-Interceptor Wing USAF, who flew the Sabre, finishing the war with fifteen MiG-15s downed. Of the F-86Fs built, a large number went to other air forces under MDAP and Mitsubishi of Japan produced F-86Fs and three-camera reconnaissance RF-86Fs under license.

The F-86H was basically a fighter-bomber development of the F-86F, powered by a 4218kg (9300lb) thrust General Electric J73-GE-3 engine. It had a 15cm (6in) deeper fuselage, larger tailplane without dihedral, greater length, electrically-operated flaps, hydraulically-operated speed brakes and controls, refined ejector seat for the pilot, strengthened landing gear, improved mechanism for carrying drop tanks together with rockets and bombs and fixed armament increased during production from six guns to four 20mm M-39 cannon. The first prototype flew on 30 April 1953 and 473 production examples were built between September 1953 and August 1955.

The final production version of the Sabre to be built in the United States was the F-86K, a J47-GE-33-powered update of the F-86D armed with four cannon for use by other NATO nations. North American produced 120, these going almost equally to the Netherlands and Norway, while a further 221 were assembled under license by Fiat in Italy for the Italian air force and others in Europe. The final piloted model of the Sabre was the F-86L, 981 of which were completed by modification from F-86Ds. Apart from its new slotted wing leading edge and new wingtips, which increased the span, it incorporated 'data link' equipment to receive information from the SAGE (Semi-Automatic Ground Environment) electronic air defense monitoring computer regarding intercept instructions. The only other model of the Sabre to follow the 'L' was the QF-86, the designation of surplus USAF aircraft operated as target drones.

In Australia the Commonwealth Aircraft Corporation produced 111 production Sabres powered by Rolls-Royce Avon engines and these were the fastest Sabres with maximum speeds of about 1125 km/h (700 mph), compared with the F-86A's 1086 km/h (675 mph) and F-86F's 1105 km/h (687

Left: the North American Sabre was license-built in Canada, a total of 1815 being produced by Canadair.

mph). So good were these that, when replaced by French Dassault Mirage IIIs, a number were acquired by the Indonesian air force, with whom they remained until 1978.

Canadair license-built the Sabre between 1950 and 1958, eventually producing 1815 for the RCAF and other air forces as Sabre Mk 2s (based on the F-86E and with the J47 engine), Sabre Mk 4s (similar to the Mk 2), Sabre Mk 5s (2950kg;6500lb thrust Orenda 10 engines and '6-3' wings) and Sabre Mk 6s (3270kg; 7210lb thrust Orenda 14 engines), plus Mk 1 and Mk 3 prototypes.

As mentioned earlier, the Soviet counterpart of the Sabre was the MiG-15, an excellent fighter with high performance made

Below: the Mikoyan-Gurevich MiG-15bis was built in Poland, where it was known as the LiM-2.

possible by the production of the RD-45 (Rolls-Royce Nene) engine at Moscow's No 45 factory. Whilst it is true that the MiG-15 owed its early success to the Nene engine, it should not be forgotten that the original specification under which it was designed was issued in early 1946, well before Britain delivered Nene and Derwent engines to the Soviet Union. It can be seen as a measure of the importance the Soviet Union placed on turbojet-powered aircraft, that it initiated this fighter competition so soon after the first competitions.

The Lavochkin prototype has already been mentioned. Yakovlev produced its Yak-30, which was a complete breakaway from the Yak-15 style of fighter and indeed looked very like the MiG. The MiG prototype was known as the I-310 and first flew on the second to last day of 1947 on the power of one of the original Nene engines from

Britain. A program of intensive evaluation and testing followed, matched only by the speed at which the RD-45 engine was entering production.

Mikoyan-Gurevich was virtually guaranteed the production 'go-ahead,' for the I-310 was not only a sound design but could be in production before Lavochkin and Yakovlev had prototypes ready. Production MiG-15s, initially powered by 2200kg (4850lb) thrust engines but after a short time by developed 2270kg (5004lb) thrust RD-45Fs, entered service in 1948. Armament comprised one 37mm N-37 and two 23mm NS-23 cannon in the nose, supplemented optionally by two bombs, rockets or drop tanks. The very first MiG-15s may have had two 12.7mm guns instead of the NS-23s.

Later receiving the NATO reporting name *Fagot*, the MiG-15 had mid-set wings, swept at an angle of 42 degrees at the lead-

ing edge. Two fences were attached to each wing. The circular-section fuselage was built in two main parts and the nose air intake was divided to channel air past the fuel tanks in the mid fuselage. Early fighters did not have a pilot ejection seat, but this later became a standard feature in the pressurized cockpit. Avionics comprised only a high-frequency radio and a homing receiver.

In addition to entering Soviet service, MiG-15s were supplied to North Korea and China, enabling the well documented and classic dogfights between the well-matched MiGs and Sabres from early in the Korean war. MiG-15s were also put into production in Czechoslovakia and Poland, as S-102 and LiM-1 fighters respectively.

During 1950 the original MiG-15 was replaced on production lines by the improved MiG-15bis. The main difference was in power plant, with the MiG-15bis using the 2700kg (5952lb) thrust Klimov VK-1, a further development of the Nene. Other changes included the use of perforated wing flaps, increased internal fuel capacity and more and improved avionics. Yet a reduced structural weight was achieved. Maximum speed was 1076 km/h (668 mph) and it was capable of carrying two 100kg, 250kg or 500kg bombs, rockets or 400 liter (88 Imperial gallon) drop tanks. Production lines in Czechoslovakia and Poland built S-103s and LiM-2s respectively.

In addition to the standard MiG-15 fighters, there appeared the MiG-15P all-weather version carrying Izumrud radar, the MiG-15Sbis high-altitude fighter, the MiG-15bisR armed photographic reconnaissance aircraft and the tandem two-seat MiG-15UTI trainer. The trainer, which was also built in Czechoslovakia as the CS-102,

Poland as the SBLiM-1 and in China, is the only version of the MiG-15 in widespread use today. It is worth mentioning that MiG-15bis and MiG-15UTIs completed in China were the first jets built there and that several hundred remain in use.

The MiG-15 can be viewed by historians as the springboard of modern Soviet fighter design, preparing the ground for the MiG-17, MiG-19, the most widely flown MiG-21, the swing-wing MiG-23 and the fastest fighter in the world, the MiG-25, known to NATO as *Foxbat*. But what of Lavochkin, Sukhoi and Yakovlev? After the La-15 the former name never again appeared on a production fighter. It took Sukhoi a decade to get a jet fighter into production and about as long for Yakovlev to follow its Yak-23 with a new fighter, in fact the Soviet Union's first two-seat all-weather fighter powered by two turbojet engines, as the Yak-25.

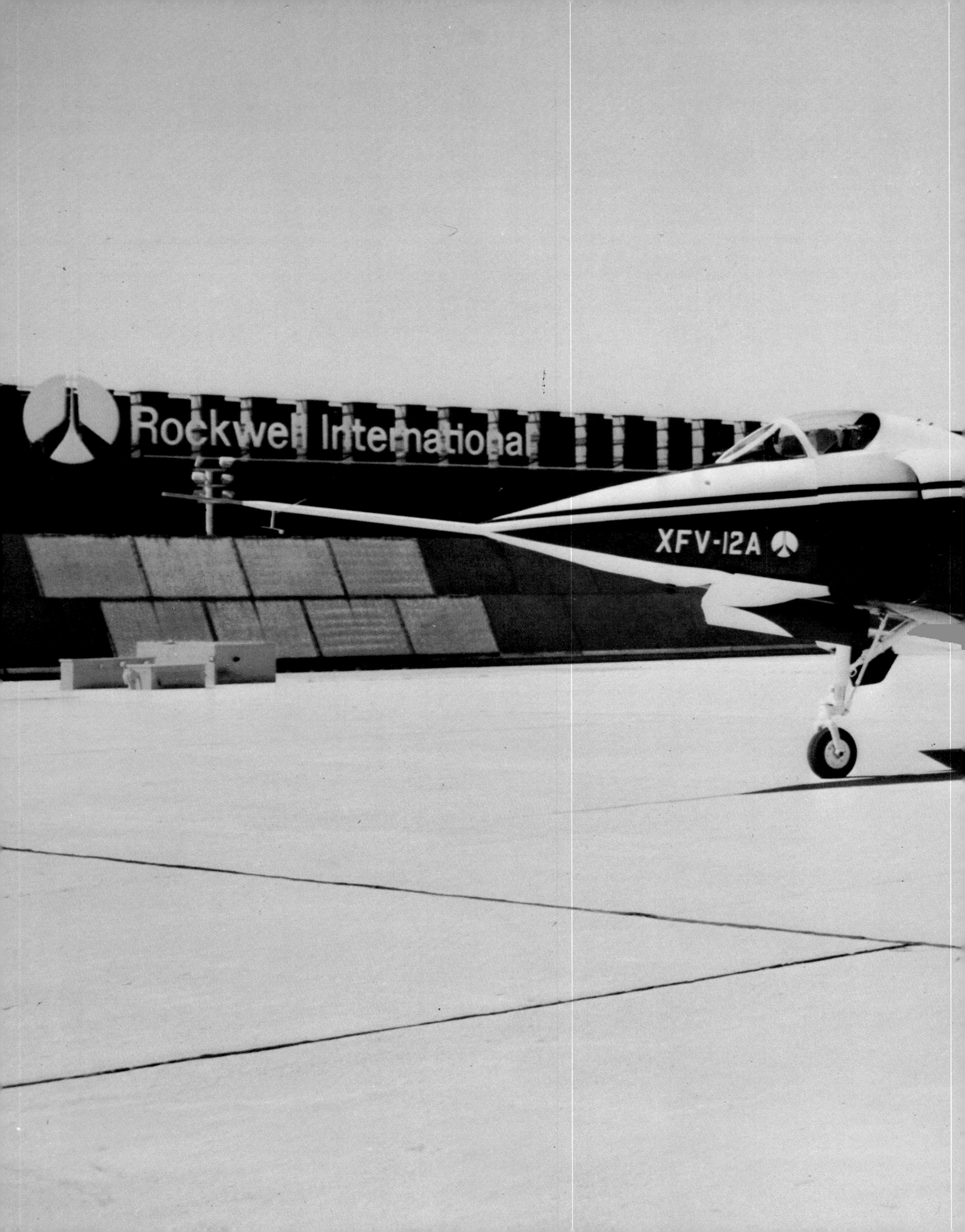
Rockwell International
XFV-12A

4: STRANGE SHAPES IN THE SKY

se of the jet engine was in its infancy when designers began to consider matching the new and highly-exciting power plant with equally non-conforming airframes. One company that saw the engine as not merely the power source for a conventional airframe was Northrop Aircraft, California, which during World War II had already begun developing aircraft with no fuselages or tail units as 'flying wings.' Most of the company's activities in this field centered around the development of huge-span flying-wing bombers, but it also developed an 11.58m (38ft) span experimental flying-wing

Overleaf: the Rockwell International XFV-12A is an experimental vertical/short take-off fighter for the US Navy.

fighter, powered by two 522kg (1150lb) thrust Westinghouse J30 turbojet engines. The pilot occupied a cockpit in the center of the wing, lying in prone position so as not to spoil the overall shape of the wing. Designated XP-79B, this experimental fighter was intended to slice-off the tails of enemy bombers, using its high-strength welded magnesium wing. In the event, it went out of control on its first flight on 12 September 1945 and the project ended. However Northrop had much more success with its flying-wing bombers, which very nearly became the subject of large orders for the USAF.

Water-based jet fighters interested many designers postwar, the bombers and fighter-bombers in use at the end of World War II showing clearly the vulnerability of airfields to attack. Britain was among the

first to appreciate the possible uses for a sea-going jet fighter, although it should be said that conventionally-powered flying-boat fighters had been around since the early stages of World War I. Saunders-Roe designed the SR.A/1 to Air Ministry specification E.6/44. This was a bulky all-metal flying-boat with shoulder-mounted straight monoplane wings accommodating semi-retractable stabilizing floats. Power was provided initially by two 1474kg (3250lb) thrust Metropolitan-Vickers Beryl axial-flow turbojets mounted in side-of-fuselage fairings below the wings. The nose air intake was protected from spray during take-off and landing by a retractable fairing.

The SR.A/1 flew for the first time on 16 July 1947, so becoming the world's first jet-powered flying-boat. Three prototypes were built, the later two with slightly more powerful engines. Following a period of development and flight trials, the fighter was abandoned. The officially stated reason for not proceeding with production was the aircraft's lack of speed and maneuverability, caused by the deep and bulky hull. Whilst it must have been true that the SR.A/1 was less maneuverable than land-based jets, its speed of 824 km/h (512 mph) was fairly respectable. But, seen in context, even during World War I flying-boat fighters of Macchi-type managed to equal land-based fighters for speed and in the late 1940s and early 1950s there was every reason to believe that jet fighters were going to get faster very rapidly.

Another company that investigated the concept of a sea-going fighter was Convair, California, its delta-winged Sea Dart flying for the first time on 9 April 1953. Convair had pioneered delta wing research in the United States after World War II, helped by Dr Alexander Lippisch who had previously been researching along similar lines in Germany. On 18 September 1948 Convair flew its Model 7002, an experimental aircraft that had been built to investigate the flight characteristics of the projected F-92 fighter. When the F-92 program was cancelled, the experimental aircraft became the XF-92A, powered initially by one 2086kg (4600lb) thrust Allison J33-A-23 turbojet engine and later by an afterburning

Above left: the Saunders-Roe SR.A/1 was the world's first jet-powered flying boat and first flew in 1947.

Left: the Convair XF-92A experimental fighter evaluated the delta wing later used for the F-102 interceptor.

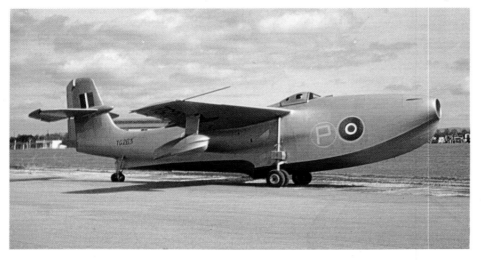

3720kg (8200lb) thrust J33-A-29. The delta wing form of the XF-92A was used subsequently by Convair for its Sea Dart and F-102 Delta Dagger fighters.

The Sea Dart itself was an experimental seaplane fighter, powered in original form by two 1542kg (3400lb) thrust Westinghouse J34-WE-42 turbojet engines. Accommodating a single pilot, it was expected to float in the water as a flying-boat during its first stages of take off, thereafter, and at a particular speed, a retractable hydroski or two hydroskis being lowered to lift the hull from the water prior to lift-off. After take off the hydroski or hydroskis were retracted back into the underside of the aircraft, allowing the Sea Dart to have a fairly normal fuselage and so maintain a high rate of maneuverability. A small number of refined Westinghouse J46-powered Sea Darts were built to extend the test program. Nevertheless the Sea Dart remained experimental,

although one had achieved Mach 1 in a shallow dive, the first seaplane to do so. So despite early promise, water-based jet fighters have never been part of an air force's inventory.

Convair was also one of two companies contracted by the US Navy to construct prototype vertical take-off and landing (VTOL) fighters, for possible use from naval vessels not fitted with conventional aircraft carrier decks. We now know that it took the British Sea Harrier (via the Hawker Siddeley Kestrel) and the Soviet Yakovlev Yak-36MP to master the naval VTOL combat aircraft role, but in the early 1950s the technology was not there to produce such advanced designs. Instead Convair, and its rival for orders Lockheed, produced what became termed 'tail-sitters.' The basic approach for the Convair XFY-1 Pogo and for the XFV-1 Vertical Riser was that the wings and tail surfaces, or the tail surfaces alone, would

Above: the Convair Sea Dart made use of hydroskis to achieve waterborne take-off from a flying boat hull.

form a cruciform shape, thereby allowing the aircraft to rest on castor wheels while pointing upward. The pilot of each aircraft sat on a gimballed (tilting) seat, so that he could assume a semi-upright position for take-off and landing, while sitting in a conventional position during normal horizontal flight. Power was provided by one Allison YT40-A-14 and one YT40-A-6 turboprop engine respectively on the Pogo and Vertical Riser, each engine driving co-axial contra-rotating propellers. It had been Dr Griffith, as mentioned in the first chapter, who had first suggested using a turbine not only to produce jet efflux but to drive a propeller via a reduction gear, back in 1926. Few fighters were actually designed to use turboprop engines, but an example of a highly-successful exponent of the turbo-prop was the British Westland Wyvern carrier-borne strike fighter of the 1950s. The Lockheed XFV-1 Vertical Riser was the more conventional of the two experimental fighters (the term 'conventional' being relative) by having straight wings as well as cruciform tail surfaces. However it was actually the least successful, first flying in March 1954 but achieving only horizontal flight before being cancelled.

The Convair XFY-1 Pogo first flew in August 1954 and in the course of the flight test program achieved its first transition from vertical to horizontal flight and back again on 2 November the same year. In typical Convair fashion, the Pogo had delta wings and smaller tail surfaces. However this aircraft too was subsequently abandoned, ending this particular US Navy program.

Several countries attempted to come up with successful VTOL designs for use on land, these including Germany's VFW-Fokker VAK 191B tactical reconnaissance fighter and the French Dassault Mirage III-V. The former first flew on 10 September 1971 and was powered by two Rolls-Royce RB.162-81 lift-jets mounted vertically in the fuselage and one horizontally-mounted RB.193-12 vectored-thrust engine for forward propulsion. Maximum speed was subsonic. It failed to enter production as a Fiat G91 replacement.

The Mirage III-V was the proposed VTOL variant of the production Mirage III fighter. Following on from the earlier Dassault Balzac research aircraft, which first flew in October 1962, the Mirage III-V was basically a lengthened and SNECMA TF-104, TF-106 or Pratt & Whitney TF30 turbofan-engined III-E, fitted with eight Rolls-Royce RB.162-1 lift-jet engines in the center section of the fuselage and covered by hinged doors. Two Mirage III-Vs were built, the first transition from horizontal to vertical flight being performed on 24 March 1966, but this variant of the highly-successful Mirage III remained experimental.

A modern US Navy program to evolve a new form of V/STOL (Vertical/Short Take-off and Landing) fighter and attack aircraft was initiated in the 1970s, resulting in the design and construction of the Rockwell

Right: the Lockheed XFV-1 Vertical Riser was one of two 'tail sitters' developed for the US Navy.

Far right: the Convair XFY-1 Pogo competed with the XFV-1 to meet the VTOL naval fighter requirement.

International XFV-12A. A single-seater with rear-mounted main wings and canard surfaces, the XFV-12A is powered by one modified 13,600kg (30,000lb) thrust Pratt & Whitney F401-PW-400 turbofan engine. For normal flight this horizontally-mounted engine exhausts from the rear tailpipe, but for vertical flight a valve closes this exit point, the efflux being diverted downward through ducts in the canards and wings.

Mixed with these gases is drawn-in ambient air, which results in greater thrust. Maximum speed of the XFV-12A is hoped to be approximately Mach 2. Unfortunately, funding shortages caused by defense program cutbacks has slowed progress.

Like France with its Mirage III-V, the Soviet Union attempted to increase the versatility of standard fighters using lift-jets. At the 1967 air display at Domodedovo,

three experimental STOL fighters and a VTOL type were flown. The Mikoyan MiG-21 (NATO *Fishbed-G*) and Mikoyan *Faithless* each used single main engines and two vertically-mounted lift-jets installed in tandem in the fuselage center section to achieve STOL performance, while the larger STOL aircraft based on the Sukhoi Su-15 (NATO *Flagon-B*) had two main engines and three lift-jets. All of these re-

mained experimental, as did the VTOL research aircraft flown during the display and built by Yakovlev. The Yak operated on the power of two forward-mounted turbojet engines, exhausting through large vectored-thrust nozzles. During the display it performed a full transition from vertical to horizontal flight and vice versa and at one point made a high-speed but subsonic dash flight. Known to NATO as *Freehand* (the 'F'

reporting name indicating a fighter role – albeit experimental), it helped Yakovlev develop the far more sophisticated Yak-36MP, which uses a mixture of the power plant installations found on these STOL and VTOL types.

Although most of the Soviet, French and German aircraft described previously had mixtures of horizontally and vertically-mounted engines, all the engines them-

selves were conventional turbojets or turbofans. Aircraft with truly 'mixed' power plants have been built, at the time of their appearance seeming to offer solutions to the problem of attaining high performance.

As described in chapter five, the Ryan

Below: the Dassault Mirage III-V made use of fuselage-mounted lift-jets for hovering flight

Below: the Ryan XF2R-1 Dark Shark was
powered by a nose-mounted turboprop
and a turbojet in the rear fuselage.

Fireball was built in very limited numbers as a mixed-power naval fighter. During production four Fireball airframes were assigned for experimental use, one becoming the XF2R-1 Dark Shark. First flown in November 1946, the Dark Shark had the usual General Electric J31 turbojet installed in the rear fuselage, but the nose-mounted engine was the new General Electric TG-100, a 2200shp, plus 272kg (600lb) thrust, turboprop engine which received the designation XT31-GE-2. The TG-100 was the first all-American tuboprop engine and was intended to power the aircraft during all phases of flight, except when increased speed was required for combat. Maximum

speed of the one-off Dark Shark was approximately 805 km/h (500 mph).

In America Republic flew its experimental Mach 1 turbojet and rocket-powered XF-91 interceptor in 1949, featuring also variable-incidence and inverse-tapering swept wings, and Britain built and flew a turbojet and rocket-powered interceptor in the form of the experimental Mach 2.4 Saunders-Roe S-R.53, which first flew on 16 May 1957. However the French were the main protagonists of mixed power. One such aircraft was designed in the latter 1940s as the Sud-Ouest SO 9000 Trident, a mixed-power research aircraft that was intended to lead to the development of a

similarly-powered interceptor. The original Trident was a fairly unspectacular aircraft, with straight constant-chord wings and a circular-section fuselage ending with an all-moving three surface tail unit. Power was initially provided by two 400kg (880lb) thrust Turboméca Marboré II turbojets installed in wingtip pods, subsequently replaced by Dassault M.D.30 Viper ASV.5s with twice the power. On the power of the Marboré IIs, the Trident first flew on 2 March 1953. Prior to the change to Vipers a 4500kg (9921lb) thrust SEPR.481 rocket motor had been installed in the tail, a flight being achieved in this form on 4 September the following year. During the spring of 1955

it broke the sound barrier while in a shallow dive, followed soon after by Mach 1 flight while climbing.

The Trident had achieved Mach 1 on nothing like full power, so the decision was taken to develop the SO 9050 Trident II as the prototype of a lightweight interceptor. Two were ordered, one of which was de- stroyed in an accident when the rocket fuel exploded. By the time of the accident the first of six preproduction Trident II inter- ceptors had already flown on 3 May 1957, indicating a maximum speed of very nearly Mach 2. One Trident II, powered by 1100kg (2425lb) thrust Turboméca Gabizo turbojets and an SEPR 631 rocket motor, established a new world altitude record by reaching 24,217m (79,452ft) on 2 May 1958, bettering the previous record, set by a Grumman F11F-1 Tiger a fortnight before, by nearly 800 meters. Actual production Trident inter- ceptors were not built, the program having been abandoned due to defense cutbacks.

Left: the Sud-Ouest Trident was an experimental mixed-power aircraft, with turbojet and rocket motors. It is now displayed at Le Bourget.

Below: the Saunders-Roe S-R.53 was a British mixed-power interceptor, which was not produced for the RAF.

Above: the Griffon II combined turbojet and ramjet power and is shown on display at Le Bourget.

Right: the McDonnell XF-85 Goblin was a parasite fighter, which was to be carried by the B-36 bomber.

This was undoubtedly the right decision for another reason. In view of the far more advanced design of the British S-R.53, which would have carried Firestreak air-to-air missiles at the wingtips and had much higher speed, the Trident would have been out-of-date before entering service.

Another French experimental aircraft of the mid-1950s from which it might have been possible to develop an interceptor, hence the subsequent interest shown by the USAF, was the Nord 1500 Griffon II. This was little more than a huge combination power plant around which was fitted a pilot's cockpit, delta wings and a vertical tail. In fact the Griffon II was the modified turbojet only-powered Griffon I, fitted with a 3400kg (7495lb) thrust SNECMA Atar 101 turbojet engine installed inside a Nord-designed annular and integral ramjet.

The French Leduc experiments with ramjet-powered aircraft from the late 1940s, had proved the power obtainable from this form of power plant, but as a ramjet will not operate until high-velocity air is introduced through the duct, René Leduc's early aeroplanes had to be air-launched. He had expected to construct an interceptor version of his aircraft under French military contract, but this work ended after official support had been withdrawn. In fact the Griffon II first flew in the same year as Leduc's experiments were terminated in 1957. However Leduc had expected his interceptor to take off under its own power, using an Atar turbojet in combination, there-

after igniting the ramjet. It was this system that was used by the Griffon II. The Griffon's ramjet developed 4170kg (9193lb) thrust at an altitude of 15,240m (50,000ft), allowing for a very high maximum speed but which had to be kept at just over Mach 2 because of the limitation posed by the construction of the airframe. Therefore despite early promise, no production aircraft has ever had a ramjet as its primary power plant, although it has been used on missiles, an example being the British Bloodhound.

Another aircraft that, like the Griffon II, had an engine seemingly disproportionate in size to its overall dimensions, was the McDonnell XF-85 Goblin. Development of this fighter began in 1945, as one of the proposed defense systems for the Consolidated-Vultee B-36 six-engined intercontinental strategic bomber. Known as a parasite fighter, it was intended to be carried in the forward bomb-bay of the B-36. When threatened by interceptor attack, it was envisioned that the bomber would lower the Goblin out of the bay by means of a 'trapeze,' the fighter subsequently being recovered again by the use of a special retractable 'sky hook' carried in front of the pilot's cockpit. The hook-on technique had already served the United States well, when in the 1930s Curtiss Sparrowhawk biplane fighters had operated from US Navy airships.

The Goblin itself was built around a 1360kg (3000lb) thrust Westinghouse J34-WE-22 turbojet engine and had swept

Left: a model of Grumman's FSW (forward swept wing) demonstrator aircraft.

wings of only 6.47m (21ft 2¾in) span that could be folded. Six individual surfaces made up the tail unit and armament comprised five forward-firing guns. With a total length of only 4.53m (14ft 10½in) and a height of 2.52m (8ft 3¼in), it could easily fit into the B-36's bomb bay.

The concept of using a jet fighter to hook onto a fast bomber was proved by tests with a modified P-80 Shooting Star and a B-29 bomber and the Goblin was taken up by the specially adapted B-29 for its first free flight on 23 August 1948. Flying over the Muroc test base, the fighter was released. At an altitude of 7620m (25,000ft) the Goblin attempted to hook back on to the trapeze, but rough conditions caused the fighter to rise suddenly as it neared the trapeze. The force of impact as the fighter struck the trapeze caused the cockpit canopy to smash, while the pilot lost both his helmet and oxygen mask. Although the pilot had the use of an ejection seat, he elected to attempt to land the Goblin on the desert sands below, having already put what remained of the oxygen hose into his mouth. At high speed, he put the Goblin down on its emergency-only landing skids. Remarkably only a bent ventral fin and one damaged wingtip resulted. After the addition of small fins on the wings to improve stability, several successful hook-ons were made. However for whatever reason, the parasite fighter concept for the production B-36 was dropped, although the success attained during later trials must have influenced a later decision to use a version of the Republic Thunderflash as a parasite reconnaissance aircraft, to provide reconnaissance models of the B-36 with a 'dash' plane to make the final reconnaissance over the target area. In a way, by allowing the B-36 to 'stand off' from the target area, the Thunderflash acted as protection for the motherplane.

Even today when money is short for experimentation into new technologies, new shapes are emerging. Will the fighter of the 1990s have forward-swept wings, as is being researched by Grumman. In 1983 there will appear the first modern jet-powered experimental aircraft with rear-mounted swept-forward wings and canards, said to offer improved maneuverability, be virtually impossible to spin, have less drag, and have many other benefits. Only time will tell!

5: AIR POWER AT SEA

In 1917 a light battle cruiser under construction for the Royal Navy was redesignated an aircraft carrier and modified accordingly. Appearing as HMS *Furious,* it was the world's first naval vessel designed to operate land-planes from its deck, being assigned six Sopwith Pup fighters and four seaplanes. Later accommodating thirty-three aircraft, HMS *Furious* was active again during the interwar period and World War II, finally being sent to the scrap yard in 1949.

By the outbreak of World War II some 20 aircraft carriers were operational with the navies of Britain, France, Japan and the United States. Those of Japan and the United States met in the epic battles of the Coral Sea and Midway in 1942, when an American airman sent out the famous message 'scratch one flat-top' following the destruction of a Japanese carrier. Construction of at least 11 other aircraft carriers had been underway in 1939. During this war carrier operations were widespread and included

the use of lower-cost and mass produced smaller escort carriers.

For the US Navy by far the most important carrier fighter of World War II was the Grumman F6F Hellcat. It first went into action in an attack on Marcus Island in September 1943, eventually accounting for nearly three-quarters of enemy aircraft destroyed by the Navy. Potentially even more potent was the Chance Vought F4U Corsair, which was flown by the US Marine Corps initially from land bases, as the

Overleaf: the USS *Enterprise* was the world's first nuclear-powered aircraft carrier.

fighter's landing speed was considered too high for use from carriers. The Royal Navy did not share this view and from 1944 operated the Corsair from its carriers, leading the way for America to follow.

Today the US Navy has by far the biggest and most powerful aircraft carrier force in the world, each vessel carrying what can be described as a small air force. This can be made up of two interceptor-fighter squadrons flying McDonnell Douglas F-4 Phantoms or Grumman F-14 Tomcats, two

squadrons of Vought A-7 Corsair attack aircraft, one squadron of Grumman A-6 Intruder strike and tanker aircraft, plus Grumman EA-6B Prowler ECM and Grumman E-2 Hawkeye airborne early-warning and fighter control aircraft, one squadron of Lockheed S-3A Viking anti-submarine aircraft and Sikorsky SH-3 Sea King helicopters, approximately 90 aircraft in total.

The operation of jet fighters from aircraft carriers had a rather strange beginning, with Britain and the United States taking the

early initiatives. Back in 1943 the design was started of a new fighter for the US Navy, intended to make use of both piston and jet engines. Eventually known as the Ryan FR-1 Fireball, it was to be flown as an ordinary Wright R-1820 piston-engined fighter for all flying except combat dash, when the General Electric J31 installed in the rear

Below: the Ryan FR-1 Fireball was powered by a piston engine, plus a rear-mounted turbojet.

fuselage would be used. At the beginning of 1945 a squadron had been commissioned to fly the first Fireballs and trials from USS *Ranger* started. However, this squadron saw no combat during World War II. With the end of the war most of the 700 aircraft ordered in total were cancelled. Of the 66 Fireballs completed, some were used for experimental work. Although remaining in use only until 1947, finally on board USS *Badoeng Strait,* one Fireball made aviation history, when on 6 November 1945 its piston engine failed as it was making an approach to USS *Wake Island* and the pilot landed on jet power alone. This was the first occasion an aircraft using jet power had landed on a carrier, preempting the first pure jet fighter landings and take offs by a British de Havilland Vampire, to and from HMS *Ocean* by nearly a month. The Fireball had a maximum speed of 684km/h (425mph).

Whilst the British Sea Vampire became the Fleet Air Arm's first jet fighter (but not standardized in first-line service), its US equivalent was not a variant of a land-based fighter, but had been designed from the outset for naval operations. A contract to produce a prototype carrier fighter designated XFD-1 had been given to the McDonnell Aircraft Corporation in January 1943, the first of two XFD-1's flying two years later. In the following March the fighter was ordered into production as the FH-1 Phantom, becoming McDonnell's first indigenous aircraft to be series built.

On 21 July 1946 a prototype Phantom landed on board USS *Franklin D. Roosevelt,* so becoming the first US pure jet fighter to land on a carrier, and the sixty production FH-1s were operated thereafter for a brief period. Powered by two 727kg (1600lb) thrust Westinghouse J30-WE-20 turbojet engines installed in the wing roots, the Phantom had a maximum speed of 810km/h (505mph) and was armed with four 0.50in machine-guns in the nose plus optionally rockets carried under the low-mounted straight wings.

McDonnell followed the Phantom with its larger and more powerful F2H Banshee, prototypes of which had been ordered in the same month as the company had received the Phantom production order. Another straight-winged single-seater, the first Banshee prototype flew on 11 January 1947. The usual 56 production fighters were ordered as F2H-1 Banshees, each powered by two 1360kg (3000lb) thrust Westinghouse J34-WE-22 turbojets and these were delivered from early 1949. But this was just the beginning. By the close of production in

October 1953, no less than 892 Banshee fighters had been accepted by the US Navy and Marine Corps. The F2H-2 major production version with J34-WE-34 engines included night fighter and photographic-reconnaissance sub-variants.

Production was completed by the F2H-3 long-range and all-weather fighter and the

similar F2H-4, the latter receiving the most powerful engines fitted to the Banshee, in this case two 1633kg (3600lb) thrust J34-WE-38s. Armament comprised four nose-mounted 20mm cannon plus underwing weapons. The F2H-4 had a maximum speed of 981km/h (610mph), very much faster than earlier versions.

During the mid-1950s the Royal Canadian Navy took over the use of 39 F2H-3 Banshees, but by then the days of the straight-winged first-line fighter had nearly ended, even for navies. Of course straight-winged fighters other than those produced by McDonnell had entered US Navy service. Included in these were the Chance Vought F6U-1 Pirate (30 delivered from August 1949, with one Westinghouse J34-WE-30A turbojet each), the North American FJ-1 Fury, Douglas F3D Skyknight and Grumman F9F Panther. But for its Banshee replacement McDonnell designed the swept-wing F3H Demon.

The Demon was a complete break away from traditional design for McDonnell, undoubtedly helped by the design and construction of the experimental XF-88 land penetration fighter during the latter 1940s. Like the XF-88, which, in XF-88A form with afterburning, formed the basis for the USAF's F-101 Voodoo fighter, the Demon had very thin and swept wings and tail surfaces. However, unlike the XF-88, the Demon had an all-moving tailplane mounted below the fin and rudder, air intakes each side of the forward fuselage (instead of in the wing roots) and was powered by a single engine exhausting below the tail.

The first prototype XF3H-1 Demon flew on 7 August 1951. A year later an order for 150 production examples was placed, each aircraft to be powered by one 3266kg (7200lb) thrust Westinghouse J40-WE-22 turbojet. However, during development of the fighter to increase its operational capability, its weight rose from 9980kg (22,000lb) to 13,154kg (29,000lb), which left the fighter somewhat underpowered. Therefore only the first 56 production Demons used this engine. The remainder switched to the 4310kg (9500lb) thrust Allison J71-A-2, after failure of the J40-WE-24 expected replacement, as such becoming F3H-2s. Of the 56 F3H-1s, 21 were used as trainers and 29 were subsequently reengined with J71s.

The main production version of the Demon was the F3H-2, armed with four 20mm cannon and optional external stores. Sub-variants included the F3H-2N night and all-weather fighter, carrying also four AIM-9C Sidewinder air-to-air missiles and with provision for drop-tanks and nuclear weapons, and the F3H-2M day missile fighter carrying four AIM-7C Sparrow III air-to-air missiles. A projected version of the Demon was the F3H-2P photographic-reconnaissance aircraft. Altogether more than 500 Demons were built, serving in diminishing numbers until the mid-1960s, when the remaining fighters carried F-3 designations.

The Demon gave way to the mighty F-4 Phantom II, the US Navy's first Mach 2

Above far left: the McDonnell F2H Banshee first flew in January 1947 and entered service two years later.

Above left: the first American pure jet fighter to land on a carrier was the McDonnell FD-1 Phantom. This is an artist's impression.

Left: a McDonnell F3H Demon about to leave the flight deck of its parent carrier.

Below: US Navy and US Marine Corps McDonnell Douglas F-4B Phantom IIs fly alongside a USAF F-4C.

fighter and undoubtedly one of aviation's all-time greats. When first conceived in 1954, the Phantom II was to be a twin-engined all-weather attack aircraft, carrying the appropriate Navy designation AH-1. In the following year its role was changed to that of missile fighter, whereupon prototypes were ordered as tandem two-seat XF4H-1s. The first XF4H-1 flew on 27 May 1958. After early trials had necessitated some changes to the airframe, the aircraft took on its now familiar look, with low-mounted wings that were virtually a cross between swept and delta and incorporating outer panels with considerable dihedral. Its tailplane had massive anhedral, ahead and below which the two J79 turbojet engines exhausted. Both intake and nozzle areas of the ducts accommodating the engines were fully variable. Altogether 23 pre-production and 24 early production aircraft were produced for the Navy as F4H-1Fs with J79-GE-2 engines, subsequently being redesignated

F-4A Phantom IIs and carrying normally four Sparrow III missiles recessed into the fuselage underside. The first major production version was the F-4B (originally F4H-1), powered by two J79-GE-8 turbojets. This became a standard all-weather fighter with the US Navy and Marine Corps, 649 eventually being built. Normal armament comprised six Sparrow III or eight Sidewinder missiles, although up to 7257kg (16,000lb) of other weapons could be carried beneath the wings and fuselage. Of the production total, twelve temporarily became F-4Gs with data link communications equipment for use in Vietnam from USS *Kitty Hawk,* while more recently 227 have been updated as F-4Ns, redelivery taking place from 1973. Similar to the F-4B but without dual controls or missiles is the RF-4B, the USMC multi-sensor reconnaissance variant of which 46 were built as such.

In 1966 McDonnell flew an improved version of the F-4B, the F-4J, which like the

earlier Phantom II was intended primarily as a US Navy/USMC interceptor but with much improved ground attack capability. Power was provided by two 8119kg (17,900lb) thrust J79-CE-10 turbojets. Its landing speed was lowered by the use of drooping ailerons and a slotted tail, despite the fact that its weight had increased substantially. Five hundred and eighteen were built, although many have been modified to F-4S standard to extend the aircraft's useful life, changes including a strengthened structure, the use of newly-designed leading-edge slats and other updates to the airframe and avionics. Redelivery began in 1978. The only other navy to fly Phantom IIs was the Royal Navy, which received 52 F-4Ks. Designated Phantom FG.Mk 1 in British service, the first squadron was declared operational in 1969. However, with the decommissioning of HMS *Ark Royal,* the Royal Navy Phantom IIs were passed to the RAF. Similar to the US F-4B, the F-4K incor-

Below: the Phantom FG.Mk. 1 was a
Rolls-Royce Spey engined version of the
F-4 for the Fleet Air Arm.

Above: the Northrop YF-17 lightweight fighter was developed in competition with the General Dynamics F-16.

porates some improvements developed for the F-4J, and other refinements, and is powered by two 9305kg (20,515lb) thrust with afterburning Rolls-Royce Spey RB.168-25R Mk 201 turbofan engines.

By the end of Phantom II production in the United States in October 1979, 5057 had been built. Of these the US Navy and USMC had received a staggering 1264. However, twice this number had been acquired by the USAF and the remainder had been exported. Air Force versions are described in chapter six.

The very latest McDonnell Douglas combat aircraft for naval use are the AV-8B (described with the BAe Sea Harrier) and the F/A-18 Hornet. Developed out of the Northrop YF-17 lightweight fighter, which was formerly under development as a rival for the General Dynamics YF-16 for USAF orders, the single-seat Hornet was conceived by Northrop and McDonnell Douglas jointly, the latter company becoming prime contractor. However, it is not a lightweight fighter, but a full carrier-based naval strike fighter to replace the F-4 Phan-

Below: the Douglas F3D-2Q Skyknight, displayed in California, was modified for electronic countermeasures.

Above: the McDonnell Douglas F/A-18 Hornet will become the standard US Navy carrier-based strike fighter.

tom II, McDonnell Douglas A-4 Skyhawk light attack bomber and the Vought A-7 Corsair II attack aircraft.

It had been intended originally to produce two separate versions of the Hornet for fighter and attack roles, as the F-18 and A-18 respectively, but the types became so alike that a single Hornet was then proposed under the production designation F/A-18A. The TF/A-18A is the tandem two-seat training version, while the Canadian Armed Forces ordered the Hornet to replace its CF-101s and CF-104s under the designation CF-18.

The F/A-18A Hornet itself is powered by two 7257kg (16,000lb) thrust General Electric F404-CE-400 low bypass turbofan engines and is characterized by its twin outward-canted fins and rudders. Maximum speed is more than Mach 1.8. Armament as a fighter includes two Sidewinder missiles carried at the wingtips and up to four Sparrows attached underwing and on the air intakes. In an attack role up to 7710kg (17,000lb) of weapons can be carried. A nose-mounted 20mm M61 six-barrel

cannon is standard.

The first of 11 development Hornets took to the air initially on 18 November 1978 and sea trials followed in 1979. Low volume production began soon after, with the US Navy receiving its first few production Hornets for evaluation during 1980-81. Initial operational capability for the Hornet with the US Navy was planned for 1982, when deliveries to Canada were to begin.

It was during the production of the F-4 Phantom II that the name of the manufacturer changed from the McDonnell Aircraft Company to the McDonnell Douglas Corporation, when McDonnell merged with the Douglas Aircraft Company (in 1967). Douglas itself had been involved in the production of jet fighters for the US Navy and Marine Corps since the late 1940s, its first success being the F3D Skyknight. As mentioned earlier, the Skyknight was just one of several straight-winged fighters operated by the US Navy/USMC, but was unique in having side-by-side seats for the pilot and radar operator. First flown on 23 March 1948, it was armed with four 20mm cannon, although provision was made for attack weapons to be carried underwing. A dozen were also subsequently updated to carry air-to-air missiles as F3D-1Ms. During

its career the Skyknight recorded several 'firsts', including the first MiG-15 shot down at night during the Korean War, and during the early 1960s became the first tactical ECM jet aircraft. As an ECM type it remained in service long enough to be deployed in Vietnam, by which time all remaining Skyknights had received F-10 designations.

Most of the 265 Skyknights built were of the slightly more-powerful F3D-2 variant, using two 1542kg (3400lb) thrust Westinghouse J34-WE-36 turbojets mounted Scorpion-style on the lower fuselage sides, beneath the wings. But for its follow-on fighter design Douglas abandoned straight wings and conventional tail surfaces for a form of slightly swept and rounded delta wings and a vertical tail only. These very low aspect ratio wings were seen as best to combine a high rate of climb and good maneuverability with reasonable landing speeds. This layout was retained for the later Skylancer fighter, of which four development aircraft only were built as F5D-1s from 1956. But, as originally evolved, this configuration was used on the F4D Skyray, the first prototype of which first flew on 23 January 1951 on the power of a rear fuselage-mounted Allison J35-A-17 turbojet.

Left: the Grumman F9F Panther was the first US Navy jet to go into combat, during the Korean War.

Below: this Grumman F9F Panther carries 5in rockets under its wings for ground attack.

Right: a Douglas F4D-1 Skyray all-weather fighter is armed with Sidewinder air-to-air missiles.

The Skyray had been intended to be powered by a Westinghouse J40 turbojet and indeed the two prototypes flew with versions of the J40 during trials. The second, powered by a J40-WE-8 with afterburner, broke the world speed record on 3 October 1953 with a flight of 1212km/h (753mph) over a 3km course. But, despite this success, the J40 engine did not meet its early promise and the 419 F4D-1 Skyrays for the US Navy/ Marine Corps had either 6123kg (13,500lb) thrust (with afterburning) Pratt & Whitney J57-P-2 or 6577kg (14,500lb) thrust J57-P-8 engines. The first F4D-1 flew on 5 June 1954 but delivery to the Navy took nearly two more years. As with the other fighters flying in 1962, Skyrays were redesignated to conform to a new designation system, becoming F-6As. In addition to carrier use, the Skyray was flown with the North American Air Defense Command as an all-weather interceptor, in the hands of a US Navy squadron assigned to this role. It ended its operational career in about 1964, having been transferred to reserve units. Maximum speed was just over Mach 1 and armament comprised four 20mm cannon normally, but this could be complemented with up to 1814kg (4000lb) of attack weapons.

Douglas had had a close connection with the US Navy since the early 1920s, although mainly in the field of bombers and torpedo-bombers. Even closer Navy traditions has been the prize of the current Grumman Corporation, fighters built by the company under the earlier name Grumman Aircraft Engineering Corporation having been the mainstay of the Navy since the 1930s. These had included the FF-1 and later biplanes, the F4F Wildcat and the F6F Hellcat, of which the latter was rivalled by none during Navy actions of World War II.

In the long-held tradition by Grumman of using names of animals in the cat family for its fighters, its first jet fighter was known as the F9F Panther (following on from the Navy piston-engined F8F Bearcat). Originally conceived to be powered by no less than four Westinghouse 19XB-2B engines (J30s) in the wings, the design was changed to use one turbojet in the tail following the acquisition from Britain of two Rolls-Royce Nenes. In 1947 Pratt & Whitney Aircraft received a license to manufacture and sell the Nene in the United States, the first engines going to Grumman for the Panther. Pratt & Whitney

Right: the Grumman Cougar was the swept-wing version of the Panther: an F9F-8 with a radome beneath the nose is illustrated.

Nenes were known as JT-6B Turbo-Wasps, carrying the military designation J42s.

Of three Panther prototypes built, two flew with Nenes and one with an Allison J33. The first Nene-powered aircraft took to the air on 24 November 1947. Production was split between J42-P-6-powered F9F-2s and J33-A-8-powered F9F-3s, resulting in well over 400 aircraft. The first J42 and J33-powered production Panthers had flown in November and August 1948 respectively, by which time a 150 hour qualification test on the J42 at the Naval Air Material Center had proved a static thrust of 2268kg (5000lb). This was higher than the J33's 2087kg (4600lb) thrust. Indeed it was the highest publically-known thrust rating of any US engine at that time. In consequence, the F9F-2 proved to be the better fighter and F9F-3s, built to guard against J42 failure (the Navy having shown extra caution after its J30 episode), were later reengined with J42s.

No F9F-4s, which would have received Allison engines, were built. Instead the order for 73 was added to that for 580 Pratt & Whitney J48-engined F9F-5s. The J48 (Pratt & Whitney JT-7 Turbo-Wasp) was of very similar size to the J42, although rated at 2835kg (6250lb) thrust. It was similar to the British Rolls-Royce Tay, having been developed by both British and US companies. The main Pratt & Whitney contribution was probably the engine's afterburner, but the engine's main achievement was the ability

to take in 30 percent more air, made possible by a redesigned impeller and larger turbine blades. The F9F-5 was therefore the fastest version, with a maximum speed of 932km/h (579mph). Armament of all versions was four 20mm cannon, plus the provision for 5in rockets, bombs and other attack weapons. A photographic reconnaissance version became the F9F-5P.

The Panther has several claims to fame. It was Grumman's first jet fighter, the first jet fighter flown by the US Navy to see combat in Korea, the first Navy jet to destroy a MiG-15 during that war (on 9 November 1950) and the first Navy straight-winged jet fighter to be developed into a swept-wing type. Its swept-wing derivative was the F9F Cougar, of which 1985 examples were built if the 399 F9F-8T (later TF-9J) two-seat fighter-trainers are included. The first version to fly, on 20 September 1951, was the 3289kg (7250lb) thrust J48-P-8-engined F9F-6, followed by its unarmed photographic-reconnaissance equivalent, the F9F-6P. Next came the lower-powered 2880kg (6350lb) thrust Allison J33-A-16A-engined F9F-7, built in much smaller number. The last single-seaters were the faster and longer-range F9F-8 and F9F-8P, based on the F9F-6 and F9F-6P but with many refinements including increased fuel capacity in the slightly longer fuselage and the use of fixed cambered leading-edge extensions in place of the previous slats. The first F9F-8 flew on 18 January 1954, followed by the

F9F-8P on 21 August 1955. Interestingly the two-seat TF-9J Cougar was still in service as a combat and operational trainer in the early 1980s, capable of carrying rockets, bombs, four Sidewinder missiles or other stores, in addition to its two 20mm cannon.

Yet another development of the Panther was the F11F Tiger, although when this flew in prototype form on 30 July 1954 there was little to indicate this relationship. The Tiger was not very successful, with only about 200 being built for the Navy. A single 4763kg (10,500lb) thrust (with afterburning) Wright J65-W-18 turbojet engine powered all Tigers except for the prototypes, while all but the first 39 had extended noses to accommodate radar. In the event no radar was ever fitted, making the Tiger strictly a day fighter. Those which remained in 1962 were redesignated F-11As, but these were not in first line use, having been withdrawn in 1959. Nevertheless the Tiger managed a maximum speed of 1207km/h (750mph), could carry four Sidewinder missiles in addition to its four 20mm cannon, or could be used in a ground attack role. Interestingly an early Tiger fitted with a General

Above: the Grumman F11F-1 Tiger was a further development of the basic Panther design.

Right: a Grumman F-14A Tomcat fleet defense fighter prepares to catapult from a US carrier.

Electric J79 engine, as one of two experimental F11F-1Fs, set up a world altitude record in 1958 by reaching 23,449m (76,932ft), while it was reported in 1958 that Mitsubishi of Japan then expected to license-build the F11F for the JASDF.

The latest Grumman naval fighter is of course the F-14 Tomcat, which first flew in prototype form on 21 December 1970 and has become the US Navy's first multi-role fighter with variable-geometry wings. A two-seater, with the pilot and flight officer in tandem, the production F-14A has a maximum speed of about Mach 2.4 on the power of two 9480kg (20,900lb) thrust (with afterburning) Pratt & Whitney TF30-P-412A turbofan engines. Armament comprises one M61-A-1 Vulcan 20mm multibarrel gun, plus six Phoenix and two Sidewinder, or four Sidewinder and four Sparrow, or six Sparrow and two Sidewinder air-to-air missiles, or other weapons up to a maximum of 6577kg (14,500lb). The F-14A first joined the US Navy in 1972 and by September 1974 two squadrons were serving on board USS *Enterprise*. By the beginning of 1982 the Navy had received 416 F-14A Tomcats, while a further eighty had been exported to Iran by 1978 for air force use.

As mentioned earlier, Grumman was first

to use basically the same aircraft with straight and swept wings, but another company that achieved this successfully was North American Aviation. This company's first jet fighter was the FJ-1 Fury for the Navy, a contemporary of the F6U Pirate, and which beat the Panther into the air by a year. The first XFJ-1 Fury prototype flew for the first time on 27 November 1946, eventually being followed by thirty production FJ-1s to serve on USS *Boxer*. Each production Fury was powered by a 1814kg (4000lb) thrust Allison J35 engine installed in the fuselage and fed with air from the large nose intake. Maximum speed was 880km/h (547mph), sufficient to interest the USAF also, leading to the development of the Air Force's swept-wing P-86 Sabre.

In a strange turn of events, from the Air Force's Sabre was developed the Navy's

Above: the North American F-1 Fury naval fighter was a parallel development to the USAF's F-86.

swept-wing Fury, the first FJ-2 Fury prototype being flown on 14 February 1952. Production FJ-2s for the USMC were similar to the USAF's F-86E and were each powered by one 2722kg (6000lb) thrust General Electric J47-GE-2 turbojet. The remainder of the 1115 swept-wing Furies built by 1958 was made up of FJ-3s and FJ-4s, powered by Wright J65 engines. The 3493kg (7700lb) thrust Wright J65-W-16A-powered FJ-4B possessed a maximum speed of 1094km/h (680mph); it was armed with four 20mm cannon plus four Sidewinder missiles or bombs and other attack weapons optionally. The swept-wing Fury went to sea from 1954-55 with USMC and Navy squadrons, those remaining in 1962 receiving the new designation F-1.

Chance Vought's somewhat limited success with its F6U Pirate led the company to try and break new ground with its follow-up fighter. The result was the very unconventional F7U Cutlass, a swept-wing and tailless single-seater with combined ailerons and elevators (known as 'ailavators') and two fin

Below: a pair of LTV F-8 Crusaders prepare to catapult with wings in the high incidence position.

Above: the Chance Vought F7U Cutlass was the first US Navy production fighter able to exceed the speed of sound.

and rudder units mounted approximately one-third the way along the wings. The first of three XF7U-1 prototypes flew on 29 September 1948, followed by 14 F7U-1s for carrier evaluation and training duties from 1952, each powered by two Westinghouse J34-WE-32 turbojets. The next Cutlass, the 2087kg (4600lb) thrust J46-WE-8A-engined F7U-3, was the main production version, accounting for 180 of the 304 production fighters built. Larger than the F7U-1, it had folding wings and carried armament of four 20mm cannon and a pack of Mighty Mouse air-to-air rockets under the fuselage. Two further rocket packs or other weapons could be carried underwing for attack missions. Delivery of the F7U-3 began in 1954, followed by 12 photographic reconnaissance variants as F7U-3Ps. The last

production version of the Cutlass was the F7U-3M, basically the F7U-3 with provision for four Sparrow missiles. Maximum speed of the F7U-3 was 1094km/h (680mph). Despite its looks, the Cutlass was the US Navy's first production fighter capable of Mach 1, its first jet capable of delivering bombs at Mach 1, and its first jet capable of being catapult launched while armed with 2268kg (5000lb) of bombs for a strike mission.

Before merging with Ling-Temco Electronics, to form Ling-Temco-Vought in 1961, Chance Vought had in production its F-8 Crusader, a remarkable aircraft with a two-position adjustable-incidence high-mounted wing. By having the wing in its 'up' high angle-of-attack position, take off and landing speeds could be reduced while leaving the fuselage (and pilot's line of

Above: an LTV F-8E (FN) Crusader fighter of the French navy.

sight) level with the carrier deck. Designed to fulfil a US Navy requirement for a supersonic carrier-based air-superiority fighter, the first Crusader prototype flew for the first time on 25 March 1955. Altogether 1259 production Crusaders were built, including 42 exported to France (able to launch Matra R 530 and Sidewinder missiles) but not including modernized versions. Production for the US Navy began with the F-8A, the only version to have more than 300 built, which became operational in 1957. Powered by one Pratt & Whitney J57-P-12 or J57-P-4A turbojet, rated at 7257kg (16,000lb) thrust and 7327kg (16,200lb) thrust respectively, it was a day fighter only. A photographic reconnaissance sub-variant was the RF-8A. In the early 1980s, surviving F-8As were used as TF-8A trainers. The 'A' was followed by the J57-P-4A-powered F-8B, which featured an improved radar, and the F-8C day fighter with a 7665kg (16,900lb) thrust J57-P-16 engine and featuring two ventral fins.

The first limited all-weather version of the Crusader was the F-8D, powered by an 8165kg (18,000lb) thrust J57-P-20 engine. The F-8E became the second most numerous US Navy version, although, if the French Navy F-8E(FN)s are added, it actually outnumbered the F-8A. It was basically an improved F-8D with an enlarged radome. Armament of this version was four 20mm cannon plus four Sidewinder missiles carried on the fuselage, although later F-8Es were also given provision for heavy and medium bombs or rockets. Subsequent Crusaders were all modernized versions of earlier types and included the F-8H (used also by the Philippines), F-8J, F-8K and F-8L. Maximum speed of the F-8E was about 2127km/h (1322mph). In the early 1980s France still operated 25 F-8E(FN)s, the Philippines operated 24 F-8Hs as fighterbombers, while the US Navy had surviving reconnaissance RF-8Gs only.

Prior to acquiring Crusaders, France had been one of a very small band of countries that had built fighters to serve on board its own carriers. SNCASE, which had built

Vampire fighters soon after the end of World War II, later also constructed under license slightly modified versions of the de Havilland Sea Venom under the type name Aquilon. All Aquilons were powered by Italian-built Ghost 48 Mk 1 turbojets, rated at 2200kg (4850lb) thrust, and standard armament was four 20mm cannon and eight rockets. The first Aquilon flew on 31 October 1952. Production began with 50 two-seat Mk 20s and Mk 202s, the latter only for use on board carriers. Delivery of the Mk 202s ended in the spring of 1956, when production began of 40 sea-going Mk 203 single-seaters, equipped with more advanced radar and capable of carrying two Matra 5103 air-to-air missiles. The only other version was the Mk 204 unarmed twoseat trainer, bringing the total number of Aquilons to 109. Maximum speed of the fighter was 960km/h (597mph).

The Aquilon was replaced on French aircraft carriers by the Crusader and the French-designed Dassault-Breguet Etendard IV-M, the carriers *Clemenceau* and *Foch* (commissioned in 1961 and 1963)

carrying one flight of each type alongside Breguet Alizé anti-submarine aircraft. The Etendard had originally been designed as a strike-fighter for operation from land bases, but the only version to enter production was the modified Navy Etendard IV-M, which had flown as a prototype on 21 May 1958. Altogether 74 Etendard IV-Ms were built, equipping two operational units and a land-based training unit. Each was powered by one 4400kg (9700lb) SNECMA Atar 8B turbojet and carried two 30mm cannon, Sidewinder missiles or up to 1360kg (3000lb) of attack weapons. A reconnaissance and tanker version became the Etendard IV-P.

In 1973 the French Navy requested an improved Etendard to replace both the original version and the Crusader. First flown in production form on 24 November 1977, the Super Etendard is powered by one 5000kg (11,023lb) thrust SNECMA Atar 8K-50 turbojet. It also has improved high-lift devices, a sophisticated nav/attack integrated avionics system, increased range, and can receive and give in-flight refuelling. Armament combinations can include Magic air-to-air missiles, rocket pods, an Exocet anti-shipping missile, or four 400kg and two 250kg bombs. Like the Etendard IV-M, its maximum speed is about Mach 1. By May 1981 all but 20 of the 71 Super Etendards on order for the French Navy had been delivered. Fourteen were also ordered by Argentina in 1979.

A more recent advocate of the aircraft carrier has been the Soviet Union, which, during the 1970s launched its first two 40,000

Above: a de Havilland Sea Vixen F(AW). Mk. 2 all-weather fighter.

ton carrier/cruisers *Kiev* and *Minsk.* Far more akin to the new Royal Navy *Invincible* class of vessel than the huge US Navy carriers, these operate helicopters and the fairly new Yakovlev Yak-36MP (NATO *Forger-A*) single-seat VTOL combat aircraft. *Forger-A* uses a horizontally-installed main turbojet, exhausting through two vectoring nozzles to the rear of the wings and two vertically-mounted lift-jets. With a maximum speed of about Mach 1.1, *Forger-A* could have many uses, its two wing pylons being capable of carrying guns, air-to-air missiles, rocket packs and other stores. The NATO name *Forger-B* relates to a two-seat training variant.

Besides the United States, Britain has produced the greatest number of naval jet fighters. The Sea Vampire has already been mentioned. It was followed from the de Havilland stable by the D.H.112 Sea Venom, the naval version of the land-based Venom. Evolved as an all-weather fighter from the two-seat Venom NF.Mk.2, the Royal Navy first received 2200kg (4850lb) thrust de Havilland Ghost 103-powered F(AW). Mk. 20s and F(AW).Mk.21s, the latter with power-operated controls, special avionics, a power jettisonable cockpit hood and ejection seats. The F(AW).Mk.22, with a more-powerful Ghost 105 engine, followed. These served until 1960. The French also built Sea Venoms as Aquilons, while the Royal Australian Navy received a version of the F(AW).Mk.21 as the Mk.53.

De Havilland's D.H.110 two-seat all-weather day and night fighter followed the Sea Venom into Royal Navy service, having completed aircraft carrier trials in the spring of 1956. Powered by two Rolls-Royce Avon 208 turbojets mounted side-by-side in the rear of the fuselage nacelle, it followed de Havilland's predilection for the twin-boom configuration. The pilot occupied a cockpit offset to port, while the second crew member sat within the fuselage to starboard. Production of the Sea Vixen for the Royal Navy lasted until 1964, initially covering 119 F(AW). Mk.1s, each carrying 28 2in rockets on retractable underfuselage racks plus up to four Firestreak air-to-air missiles, or optionally various combinations of extra rockets, missiles and attack weapons. Twenty-nine longer-range F(AW).Mk.2s had Red Tops as their missile armament. Sea Vixens became operational from 1959.

Despite the many 'firsts' de Havilland jet fighters can claim, it was the Supermarine Attacker that became the first British standard single-seat carrier jet fighter. Originally conceived to use the Rolls-Royce Nene as an RAF fighter, it made use of the straight wings and tailwheel landing gear developed for the piston-engined Supermarine Spiteful/Seafang. The first Attacker flew on 27 July 1946 as an RAF prototype, but

Left: the de Havilland Sea Venom was a navalized version of the RAF's Venom night fighter.

Right: Supermarine Attacker F.Mk. 1s were the first standard, single-seat jet fighters in the Fleet Air Arm.

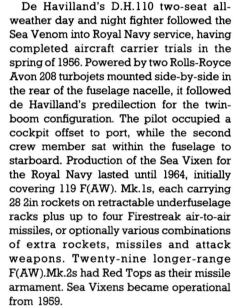

the following two prototypes conformed to Navy requirements. Carrier trials on board HMS *Illustrious* took place in 1947. The type entered service from 1951 in Attacker F.Mk.1 interceptor and then, from 1952, in Attacker FB.Mk.1 fighter-bomber versions, each with one 2313kg (5100lb) thrust Nene 3 turbojet in the fuselage. The later Attacker FB.Mk.2 used the Nene 102. The 61 Attacker Mk.1s for the Royal Navy were armed with four 20mm cannon plus two 1000lb bombs or several 60lb rockets underwing, while FB.MK.2s could carry up to 12 rockets in addition to the other weapons. Maximum speed of the FB.Mk.2 was 950km/h (590 mph). A further 36 Attacker F.Mk.1s were built, these serving with the Royal Pakistan Air Force.

Supermarine followed the Attacker with the Scimitar for the Royal Navy, a far more ambitious single-seat interceptor and strike aircraft. Powered by two 5103kg (11,250lb) thrust Avon Mk 202 turbojets, it became the Navy's first swept-wing jet when it entered service in 1958, initially operating from HMS *Victorious* in 1959. In total 76 Scimitars were built. Each was capable of a maximum speed of 1143km/h (710mph), and was armed as an interceptor with four 30mm Aden guns and optionally 96 air-to-air rockets or later four Sidewinder missiles.

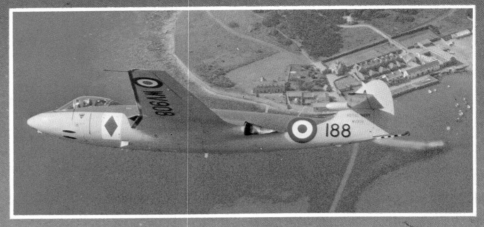

Below: Hawker Sea Hawk Mk. 100s of the West German Navy operated from land bases.

Top: a Hawker Sea Hawk F(GA). Mk. 4 flies over St Michael's Mount on the Cornish coast.

Above: Supermarine Scimitar F. Mk. 1 strike fighters entered Fleet Air Arm service in 1958.

As a strike aircraft the Scimitar could carry air-to-surface missiles, conventional or tactical nuclear bombs, or rockets. Scimitars were retired from first-line service in 1965.

Perhaps the greatest early British success story in the naval jet fighter field was the Hawker (Armstrong Whitworth) Sea Hawk, a straight-winged single-seat fighter that entered service with the Royal Navy, Royal Netherlands Navy, Indian Navy (including ex Royal Navy and German Navy aircraft) and German Navy. It was finally to be found on board the Indian Navy carrier *Vikrant*, serving in an attack role into the early 1980s. Designed by Hawker Aircraft but manufactured from 1953 by Armstrong Whitworth, the Sea Hawk first flew as a prototype in 1947. The Royal Navy went on to receive 95 Sea Hawk F.Mk.1 and 40 F.MK.2 interceptors, 116 FB.Mk.3 fighter-bombers, and 183 F(GA) Mk.4 and 6 fighter-bombers, plus FB.MK.5s converted from Mk.3s. All these had Nene 101 engines except for the F(GA)Mk.6 and converted FB.Mk.5, which used Nene 104s and 103s respectively. Exports accounted for more than 100 aircraft. Maximum speed of the F(GA)Mk.6 was 964km/h (599mph). Armament for the Sea Hawk interceptors increased from four 20mm cannon alone to the use of rockets or

Above: a Sea Hawk F (GA). Mk. 6 ground attack fighter is shown with wings folded.

Left: a British Aerospace Sea Harrier FRS. Mk. 1 is armed with Sidewinder missiles.

Sidewinder missiles, while fighter-bombers could carry additionally 500lb bombs or other weapons.

The final aircraft described in this chapter is considered by many to represent a type of combat aircraft which will become ever more prominent as this century closes. It is the British BAe Sea Harrier, the naval counterpart of the highly-successful land-based Harrier. A V/STOL fighter, reconnaissance and strike aircraft, the Sea Harrier is now the Royal Navy's only fixed-wing combat jet and serves on board the *Invincible* class of anti-submarine cruisers. Powered by one 9752kg (21,500lb) thrust Rolls-Royce Pegasus Mk 104 vectored-thrust turbofan, it is thought to be more versatile than its Soviet counterpart, and has a maximum speed of Mach 1.25.

The first Sea Harrier flew initially on 20 August 1978 and sea trials on board HMS *Hermes* were first conducted in late 1979. Altogether the Royal Navy is expected to receive 34 aircraft, as Sea Harrier FRS.Mk. 1s, 15 serving with three front-line units on board the carriers. The Indian Navy has also ordered the Sea Harrier, its six aircraft receiving the British designation FRS.Mk.51. So-called 'ski-jump' launching ramps used on *Invincible* class vessels allow the Sea Harrier to take off at lower STOL speeds and carry heavier weapon loads, while the wide range of weapon options include Sidewinder air-to-air missiles, or air-to-surface missiles for Royal Navy aircraft and French R 550 Magic air-to-air missiles for Indian examples.

An advanced version of the Harrier for US Marine Corps (and RAF) use is also under development as the McDonnell Douglas AV-8B, which is expected to increase greatly the aircraft's weapon load and combat radius. Powered by a 9752kg (21,500lb) thrust Pegasus 11-21E engine, it is expected to achieve the required performance increases through changes to the airframe, including the use of a supercritical wing. At present only development aircraft are flying, and only time will tell if the USMC actually receives the 336 AV-8Bs it wants.

From Sea Hawk to Sea Harrier, Phantom to Tomcat, aviation history has shown that jet fighters for the navies flying from hazardous carrier decks have matched their land-based counterparts for performance time and time again, occasionally even surpassing them.

6: CENTURY FIGHTERS

The so-called Century Series of jet fighters covered six types operated by the USAF, with military designations from F-100 to F-106. These were most prominent during the 1950s and 1960s. Also covered in this chapter are the fighters from other nations that were contemporaries of this series.

The first Century Series fighter to fly in prototype form was the North American F-100 Super Sabre. Originating as a development of the Sabre, the first prototype flew on 25 May 1953, followed just five months later by the first production F-100A. This was a single-seat day fighter, powered by one 4400kg (9700lb) thrust Pratt & Whitney J57-P-7 or J57-P-39 turbojet installed in the rear fuselage. Armament comprised four 20mm cannon, plus underwing stores when

Right: a Convair F-102A Delta Dagger serving with a unit of the Air National Guard.

Overleaf: a North American F-100C Super Sabre broke the world air speed record in August 1955.

Above: the North American F-107A was an advanced Mach 2 development of the Super Sabre.

required. A photographic reconnaissance variant became the RF-100A. The first fighter-bomber, and next version was the F-100C, powered by a 7710kg (17,000lb) thrust J57-P-21A turbojet. The 'C' was given eight underwing hardpoints for up to 3402kg (7500lb) of weapons. Interestingly an F-100C broke the YF-100A prototype's world speed record on 20 August 1955 by achieving 1323km/h (822mph). This record was to last until March of the following year, when Britain easily gained the record with its Fairey Delta 2.

The major production version of the Super Sabre was the F-100D, similarly powered to the 'C' but incorporating many refinements, including an enlarged vertical tail. Armament comprised four 20mm cannon, plus four Sidewinder or air-to-air

Left: a North American QF-100D unpiloted target drone aircraft converted from an F-100D.

missiles or other weapons. In total 1274 F-100Ds were built. The only other version of the Super Sabre was the tandem two-seat F-100F operational trainer. USAF F-100s were flown in Vietnam, but the last were recently retired. However Super Sabres were supplied to other nations under MDAP and a few still fly in Turkey and Taiwan. Maximum speed of the F-100D is 1390km/h (864mph). It is worth mentioning that an experimental development of the F-100 was the F-107A, three being built as Mach 2 plus advanced fighter-bomber prototypes, with bifurcated air intakes above the fuselage and J75 engines.

Chronologically the next of the Series was the Convair F-102 Delta Dagger, which first flew in prototype form on 24 October 1953. it was the first of Convair's combat jets to use delta shaped wings, as flown on the experimental XF-92A, and 875 production F-102As were built from 1956. As with the TF-102A two-seat training version, power was provided by a single 7800kg (17,200lb) thrust (with afterburning) Pratt & Whitney J57-P-23 or J57-P-25 turbojet. Armament comprised one AIM-26B and three AIM-4C Falcon air-to-air missiles, carried internally. Delta Daggers served for many years with Air Defense Command, but by the end of

the 1970s even those passed to the Turkish Air Force had been retired. Maximum speed was 1327km/h (825mph).

From the Delta Dagger Convair developed the F-106 Delta Dart, powered by a 11,113kg (24,500lb) thrust Pratt & Whitney J57-P-17 turbojet to give a maximum speed of 2455km/h (1525mph). A total of 227 single-seat F-106A interceptors was built for Air Defense Command, the first flying on 26 December 1956, plus a number of F-106B two-seat trainers. Outwardly the F-106A could easily be identified from the F-102A by its redesigned straight-topped vertical tail and side air intakes which ended just forward of the wing leading-edges. Originally armed with one Genie or Super Genie unguided air-to-air missile and four Super Falcon missiles, many aircraft were later given a 20mm cannon. In the early 1980s the USAF still operated about 223 Delta Darts.

First flown on 7 February 1954, the Lockheed F-104 Starfighter was the third Century Series jet. However, it was destined not to enjoy the success of the other fighters with the USAF, although eventually Starfighters were to be operated by 14 other nations. Featuring a long pointed fuselage, accommodating a large turbojet engine and very short-span thin straight wings, the Star-

Above: the first Convair F-106A Delta Dart interceptor for the USAF's Air Defense Command.

Left: Lockheed F-104G Starfighters of West Germany's Luftwaffe fly in formation.

Right: this view of a Convair F-106A accentuates the type's 'area ruled' fuselage.

fighter followed closely the general arrangement of the Douglas X-3 research aircraft (flown in 1952). This configuration ensured a Mach 2 capability, but was also partly the cause of the numerous accidents that befell the fighter. However some pilots have considered the Starfighter one of the best jet fighters ever built and a 'homebuilt' privately reconstructed F-104 currently holds the world low-altitude speed record.

Early production Starfighters were split between Air Defense Command and Tactical Air Command (and exported in small numbers), the former receiving 179 F-104A single-seaters and F-104B two-seaters and the latter 98 similar F-104Cs and F-104Ds. However it took the F-104G multi-mission version to get the fighter really established,

Below: three Lockheed F-104 Starfighters of the United States Air Force fly in formation.

powered by a 7167kg (15,800lb) thrust (with afterburning) General Electric J79-GE-11A turbojet. This became a European version, being built under license in Belgium, Germany, the Netherlands and Italy, covering more than 1000 aircraft. Other production lines were set up in Canada and Japan, as well as in the United States, and other recipient nations included Denmark, Greece, Norway, Spain and Turkey. The two-seat variant was the TF-104G.

The USAF no longer operates Starfighters and those of Belgium, Denmark, the Netherlands and Norway are being replaced by General Dynamics F-16s. German and Italian F-104Gs are being retired also with the introduction of the Panavia Tornado. But Italy also license-built the final version of the Starfighter, the F-104S. Following Lockheed-built prototypes, Aeritalia produced 248 F-104Ss by 1979, entering Italian Air Force service from 1969 and 40 going to

Turkey. This uprated version of the 'G' is powered by an 8120kg (17,900lb) thrust (with afterburning) J79-GE-19 turbojet. It has a maximum speed of 2330km/h (1450mph) and carries a 20mm rotary cannon plus two Sparrow and two Sidewinder air-to-air missiles, although a wide range of other weapons can be carried on its nine stores attachment points.

Flying just after the Starfighter was McDonnell's F-101 Voodoo, a single or two-seat long-range interceptor and reconnaissance aircraft. As mentioned earlier, in mid-1946 McDonnell began the design of an experimental long-range penetration fighter as the XF-88. This first flew in October 1948. In 1950 further development of the XF-88 was cancelled, but in the following year the program was revived, producing the F-101. The first Voodoo flew on 29 September 1954. Tactical Air Command received 124 single-seat F-101As and F-

Top left: three McDonnell Voodoos fly together, with an F-101A in the foreground.

Top: the two-seat F-101B Voodoo was a two-seat interceptor for Air Defense Command.

Left: the ultimate version of the Lockheed Starfighter is the Italian-built F-104S.

101Cs, the latter suitable for low-level attack duties and with provision for carrying a tactical nuclear weapon. In 1957 the F-101B tandem two-seat all-weather interceptor flew for Air Defense Command. With TF-101B trainers, a total of 480 'Bs' was built. From 1967 some F-101A/Cs were converted into reconnaissance RF-101G/Hs for reserve units. Ex-USAF F-101Bs and trainers were also acquired by Canada, which still operated 62 at the beginning of the 1980s, although these are to be replaced by Hornets. Powered by two 6750kg (14,880lb) thrust (with afterburning) Pratt & Whitney J57-P-55 turbojets, the F-101B has a maximum speed of 1963km/h (1220mph) and is armed with two Genie unguided missiles and three Falcon missiles.

The last of the Century Series to enter production was the F-105 Thunderchief, Republic's last 'Thunder' jet. The first prototype flew on 22 October 1955 and the first 75 production single-seat tactical fighter-bombers were designated F-105Bs. These were each powered by one Pratt & Whitney J75-P-3 or J75-P-5 turbojet engine. The main production version was the F-105D, an all-weather fighter-bomber powered by one 12,030kg (26,500lb) thrust (with afterburning) J75-P-19W turbojet. This possesses a maximum speed of 2230km/h (1385mph).

Six hundred F-105Ds were built, one of the versions that make up the 180 or so Thunderchiefs still flown by the USAF. As well as having a 20mm multi-barrel cannon in the nose, it can be armed with more than 6350kg (14,000lb) of externally-carried weapons, the wide range of stores including 3000lb conventional or nuclear bombs and four Sidewinder missiles. A small number of F-105Ds were modified to carry the T-Stick II bombing system.

First flown in 1963, the F-105F was de-

Above: Republic F-105 Thunderchief fighter-bombers.

Right: a Mikoyan MiG-17 of the Egyptian air force.

Overleaf: Chinese Shenyang J-6s operating at night.

veloped as an operational two-seat trainer. Featuring a longer fuselage, an increased gross weight of 24,495kg (54,000lb) and a taller fin and rudder, the F-105F was, like the F-105D, flown widely in Vietnam. Altogether 143 'Fs' were built, a number of which were later converted into ground defense suppression aircraft for use in Vietnam, designated F-105G. The 'G' itself was the final Thunderchief variant and featured an ECM pod and four Shrike or Standard ARM air-to-surface anti-radiation missiles, enabling the aircraft to attack anti-aircraft

missile sites, a role increasingly important to the US forces in Vietnam as its air offensive gathered pace. However the Thunderchief was only one of several types of aircraft that used these missiles operationally.

Like the United States, the Soviet Union developed several new fighters during the 1950s, probably the most important of which was the Mikoyan MiG-21. However to supersede the MiG-15 on production lines, a new fighter was developed as the MiG-17. This began life as little more than a refined MiG-15, the main changes being made to the rear fuselage and tail unit to improve handling characteristics at high speed. Slightly longer than the earlier fighter, the first version received the NATO name *Fresco-A*. It was a single-seat interceptor powered by a 2700kg (5952lb) thrust VK-1 turbojet, entering service in 1953. Slight changes produced the MiG-17P (NATO *Fresco-B*), most easily identified by the

more forward position of its dive brakes. The MiG-17F (NATO *Fresco-C*) was the major production day fighter, powered by a 3380kg (7451lb) thrust VK-1A turbojet, allowing a maximum speed of 1145km/h (711mph). Armament later changed from the usual single 37mm N-37 cannon and two 23mm NR-23 cannon to three NR-23s, while beneath the wings could be carried rocket pods or 500kg (1102lb) of bombs. Limited all-weather interceptor capability came with the MiG-17PF (*Fresco-D*), which carried an improved radar in the nose. When AA-1 (*Alkali*) first generation air-to-air missiles became available, with a range of 6 to 8km (3.75 to 5 miles), a non-afterburning version of the MiG-17PF, known to NATO as *Fresco-E*, became a carrier for four. Production of the MiG-17 went on into the early 1960s, with manufacture under licence being undertaken also in Czechoslovakia, Poland and China. MiG-17s remain flying with a great many air forces, the Air Force of the People's Liberation Army (China) and the People's Navy still operating more than 1000 and several hundred respectively under the Chinese designations Shenyang J-5 (MiG-17F) and J-5A (MiG-17PF).

Soon after early MiG-17s began to appear, Mikoyan flew its MiG-19 prototype, a Mikulin AM-5-engined fighter first flown on 18 September 1953. The MiG-19 was the Soviet equivalent of the early US Century Series fighters and the British Hunter, entering service with the air defense force from 1955. The first production version attained Mach 1.1 performance on the power of two 3040kg (6702lb) thrust AM-5F turbojets, later reengined as the MiG-19F with Tumansky R-9BFs. Several other versions were produced as day and limited all-weather fighters and fighter-bombers, armed normally with one 37mm N-37 and two 23mm NR-23 cannon plus bombs and rockets for ground attack, although on the MiG-19PM four *Alkali* missiles were introduced.

Known to NATO as *Farmer*, the Soviet-built MiG-19 is currently only operated by Cuba, although Chinese-built MiG-19s serve with several air forces. It was superseded on Soviet production lines in 1958, but manufacture in China under the Shenyang J-6 designation has kept the aircraft in production. The original Chinese version was the MiG-19S, a three 30mm NR-30 cannon-firing and rocket/bomb-carrying day fighter powered by two 3300kg (7275lb) thrust (with afterburning) R-9B turbojets. This first entered service in 1962. Today the Chinese air force and navy operate an estimated 2000 MiG-19s of various models for interceptor, ground attack and reconnaissance duties.

The Nanzhang Q-5 is a Chinese fighter-bomber, that nation's first high-performance combat plane of indigenous development and manufacture, although loosely

Left: a formation of Chinese Nanzhang Q-5 fighter-bombers fly over typical terrain.

Above: a Soviet-built Mikoyan MiG-19 pictured in service with the Egyptian air force.

based on the MiG. Armament comprises two 30mm cannon, four 250kg bombs carried internally, a similar number of bombs carried externally or other stores. Maximum speed has been estimated at Mach 1.35. Known to NATO as *Fantan-A,* Q-5s entered Chinese air force and navy service in the late 1970s and have been exported to Pakistan.

Equivalent to the later US Century Series fighters, three of four single-engined Soviet fighters that appeared in prototype form during 1955-56 were the Mikoyan MiG-21, Sukhoi Su-7 and Su-9. The prototype Su-7, designated S-1, first flew in 1955 as a single-seat ground attack fighter. Preproduction aircraft were known as Su-7s, but production aircraft proper were ordered in 1958 as Su-7Bs. Considerably heavier than the MiG, the Su-7B differs further from this and the Su-9 by having sweptback wings. Several versions have appeared over the years, the Su-7BMK being one of the most important because of its ability to be operated from short and unprepared airfields. To do this it has a low pressure nosewheel tyre and can be fitted with JATO. Powered by a 10,000kg (22,046lb) thrust (with afterburning) Lyulka AL-7F-1 turbojet, allowing a maximum speed of Mach 1.6, the aircraft can carry two 750kg and two 500kg bombs or rockets in addition to its fixed pair of 30mm cannon. Known to NATO as *Fitter-A,* the Su-7B is still in service with the Soviet and other air forces.

The Su-9, which appeared about the same time as the Su-7, was designed as a single-seat all-weather fighter, entering service in the Soviet Union in 1959. Known to NATO as *Fishpot-B,* the Su-9 has delta wings and carries four *Alkali* air-to-air missiles. Power is provided by a 9000kg (19,842lb) thrust (with afterburning) AL-7F engine. The Su-9 remains in the Soviet inventory, as does a refined version known as the Su-11, which has been given the reporting name *Fishpot-C* by NATO. The Su-11 has a longer nose with less taper, housing an improved radar and is powered by an AL-7F-1 engine. Carrying two *Anab* air-to-air missiles and a drop-tank, it has a maximum speed of about Mach 1.2, although this increases to Mach 1.8 without external

Above right: the Soviet MiG-21 is the most widely used combat aircraft in the world.

Right: a Soviet Sukhoi Su-7B ground-attack fighter pictured in Egyptian air force service.

stores. It too remains in use today.

The third of the 1955-56 fighters was the MiG-21. Proving to be the most successful in terms of longevity of production and with the greatest development potential, it is the lightest in weight by far. With high-speed, a good rate of climb and maneuverability, and good handling characteristics as the aim, the MiG-21 prototype first flew on 16 June 1956 as the E-5. Just over a week later it took part in an air display over Moscow. It entered production initially as a day fighter only, armed with two 30mm cannon. Power was provided by a 5100kg (11,244lb) thrust (with afterburning) Tumansky R-11 turbojet and this became known to NATO as *Fishbed-A*.

Fishbed-A was very quickly superseded in production by the slightly more powerful MiG-21F (*Fishbed-C*), also built in Czechoslovakia and armed with one cannon and two *Atoll* air-to-air missiles or rockets. The MiG-21PF (*Fishbed-D*) introduced limited all-weather capability, so matching the Sukhois for the first time, while the MiG-21PFMA (*Fishbed-J*) was developed as a multi-role version armed with a 23mm GSh-23 gun and carrying two *Atoll* and two *Advanced Atoll* missiles or four *Advanced Atolls*, rockets, bombs, air-to-surface missiles or other weapons. Many other versions of the MiG-21 have been built for the Soviet air force and for export to many countries, including third-generation types, reconnaissance models and two-seat trainers. The MiG-21 has become the world's most used fighter and about one-quarter of all Soviet tactical fighters are of this type. The most powerful version is the MiG-21bis (*Fishbed-N*) multi-role version, powered by a 7500kg (16,535lb) thrust (with afterburning) Tumansky R-25 turbojet, giving it the Mach 2 plus performance of the developed versions. In addition to using Soviet supplied MiG-21s, China also produced a small number during the mid-1960s as Xian J-7s.

Back in 1953 the prototype of the Soviet Union's first twin-engined all-weather fighter appeared, subsequently entering production as the Yak-25 (NATO *Flashlight*). A two-seater, it had subsonic performance on the power of two underwing-mounted AM-5 or RD-9 turbojets and was armed with two 37mm cannon and an underfuselage pack of air-to-air rockets. A small number of refined Yak-27s (also

Left: MiG-21 fighters of the Egyptian air force have seen action against the Israelis.

Bottom: a Dassault Mystère IIC serving
with the French Air Force's 10e Escadre.

Below: a Mirage F1 leads a Mirage III
two-seater, Super Mystère and Mystère
IVA.

Right: a Sud Aviation SO 4050 Vautour
II-N two-seat fighter taxies to the
runway.

Flashlight) with pointed noses, increased wing spans and engines with afterburners, was also produced.

Although *Flashlight* went out of service years ago, its replacement as a two-seat twin-engined all-weather fighter that ap-

Right: the Vautour II-A was a single-seat fighter bomber version of the Sud-Aviation SO 4050.

Below: the Dassault Mirage III-A prototype was an early example of the famous Mirage III series.

peared during the early 1960s as the Yak-28P (NATO *Firebar*) is still used. Just one of the production versions of the Yak-28, which included attack aircraft known to NATO as *Brewers*, about 300 *Firebars* remain with the Soviet air force today as home defense interceptors. Carrying two *Anab* missiles, *Firebar* has Mach 1.1 performance on the power of two 5950kg (13,117lb) thrust Tumansky R-11 engines fitted below the swept wings. Another older aircraft used as a home defense type is the Tupolev Tu-28P (NATO *Fiddler*), which entered service during the 1960s and about

130 remain in use. The largest fighter ever used operationally, it is a two-seater powered by two rear-fuselage-mounted 12,250kg (27,000lb) thrust (with afterburning) turbojets, bestowing a maximum speed of 1850km/h (1150mph). Armament comprises four *Ash* air-to-air missiles.

France kept up the momentum set by its Dassault Ouragan by putting four new fighters into service during the 1950s. The first was the Dassault Mystère, flown as a prototype on 23 February 1951. The Nene or Tay-powered prototypes were followed by Mystère IICs with SNECMA Atar 101 en-

gines, mainly for the French air force. The IIC was followed into production by the Mystère IVA, of which 421 were produced with Tay and 3500kg (7716lb) thrust Hispano-Suiza Verdon 350 turbojets, most with the Verdon. The majority went into French service, although India and Israel received reasonable numbers. Maximum speed was 1100km/h (684mph). A handful of Mystère IVBs were also built with new radar and afterburners. No Mystères remain in operational use today.

From the Mystère was developed the Super-Mystère B-2, the first production air-

craft flying in 1957. Most of the 180 built went to the French air force, although Israel received a few. Powered by the 4400kg (9700lb) thrust Atar 101G turbojet engine, maximum speed was 1195km/h (743mph). Armament comprised two 30mm DEFA cannon and a pack of air-to-air rockets, plus ground attack or air-to-air missiles under

Left: the Dassault Mirage III-B was a tandem two-seat training variant of the Mirage III fighter.

Below: a line-up of Mirage III-C interceptors of France's Armée de l'Air.

the wings. The last in service were 12 ex-Israeli Pratt & Whitney J52-powered B-2s refurbished and delivered to Honduras in 1977.

The third French fighter was one of three combat versions of the Sud-Aviation SO 4050 Vautour, 70 of which were built as Vautour II-N two-seat all-weather fighters. First flown on 10 October 1956, the II-N was powered by two underwing 3500kg (7716lb) thrust Atar 101E-3s, giving it a maximum speed of 1100km/h (684mph). Armament was made up of four 30mm DEFA cannon, plus many rockets or four Matra R 511 missiles.

By far the most important of the French fighters that first appeared in the 1950s was the Dassault Mirage III, which first flew on 17 November 1956 as a single-seat all-weather prototype fighter capable of operating from short and unprepared airfields. The Mirage III remains in production today, making up the majority of the 1336 Mirage IIIs/5s/50s delivered to the French and twenty other air forces by March 1981.

The single 6000kg (13,228lb) thrust Atar 9B turbojet engine replaced the earlier-used Atar 101G for the Mirage III-A and III-C production aircraft, of which 10 and 95 were built respectively for French opera-

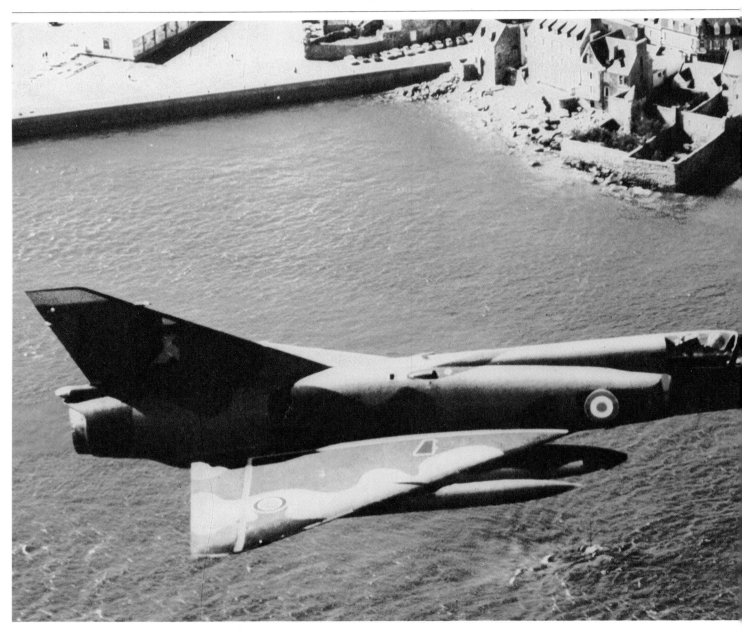

Above: a Mirage III-RD tactical reconnaissance aircraft of the French air force.

Left: Dassault Mirage 5 fighters bought by Saudi Arabia for later transfer to Egypt.

Top right: the Mirage III-EL was an export version of the III-E for the Lebanese air force.

Above right: the Mirage 50 is a multi-mission fighter intended for export, which first flew in 1979.

Right: the Saab J 32B Lansen was an all-weather interceptor fighter for the Swedish air force.

tion. Other Mirage III-Cs were delivered to Israel, South Africa and Switzerland. Versions currently available are the Mirage III-D two-seat operational trainer, Mirage III-E long-range fighter-bomber and intruder variant, and the Mirage III-R reconnaissance variant. The III-E is the most important of these, gaining its Mach 2.2 performance from its single 6200kg (13,669lb) thrust (with afterburning) Atar 9C engine. A total of 523 have been built, delivered from 1964, which include two squadrons in French service equipped to carry tactical nuclear weapons. Normal armament for interceptor duties is one Matra R 530 and two Sidewinder air-to-air missiles or the R 530 and guns.

The Mirage III introduced Dassault's now common use of low-mounted delta wings and a vertical tail only, as later fitted to the Mirage 5 ground attack development of the III-E, that was first flown in 1967, and the Mirage 50 multi-mission fighter. The Mirage 50 was first flown in 1979. Production aircraft have been delivered to Chile, with the 7200kg (15,873lb) thrust (with afterburning) Atar 9K-50 engine fitted. The latest Mirages also use delta wings, as described in the last chapter.

In Sweden during the 1950s, Saab continued its tradition of supplying that nation's air force with fighters, by following the Saab-29 with the Saab-32 Lansen. This was a completely new swept-wing combat plane, designed to the requirements as laid down by the Swedish air force and including the

Above: a Saab J 35 Draken fighter of the Swedish air force is armed with Hughes Falcon missiles.

ability to operate from major roads in an emergency. First flown on 3 November 1952, it was eventually produced in A 32A all-weather attack, J 32B all-weather fighter and night-fighter, and S 32C photographic reconnaissance versions. The J 32B was powered by one 6900kg (15,200lb) thrust (with afterburning) Rolls-Royce R.M.6B (Avon 200) engine built in Sweden, and carried 30mm cannon plus four Sidewinder missiles or rockets. Seven Swedish squadrons flew J 32Bs from 1959. By the 1980s

Lansens served only in S 32C and converted J 32D target-towing and J 32E ECM versions.

The Lansen was followed quickly by the Saab-35 Draken, a Mach 2 fighter and reconnaissance aircraft. First flown on 25 October 1955, it was given a unique double-delta wing and single vertical tail, as previously flight tested on the reduced-scale Saab-210 research aircraft. The first production version was the J 35A interceptor, which entered Swedish air force service in 1960 powered by an R.M.6B engine. This

version is no longer flown. Some were converted to Sk 35C two-seat trainer standard and others to J 35Bs, the latter an improved interceptor with a collision-course fire-control system and electronic equipment compatible with Sweden's semi-automatic air defense system. Later interceptor versions were the J 35D, with an R.M.6C (Avon 300) engine, the J 35F major production version armed with one 30mm Aden cannon and four Saab-built US-designed HM-55 and HM-58 Falcon air-to-air missiles, and the

Saab-35X export Drakens, delivered to Finland and Denmark. Those for Finland can carry two cannon, up to four Sidewinders, air-to-air rockets or ground attack weapons. With the advent of the Viggen, Swedish Drakens currently operate only as S 35E reconnaissance aircraft and Sk 35C trainers.

The first of Britain's '1950s' fighters, although flown as a prototype in September 1949, was the de Havilland Venom. Its configuration was like the earlier Vampire, but it represented a much improved design and entered RAF service from 1952 in FB.Mk 1 and Mk.4 single-seat fighter-bomber and NF.Mk.2 and Mk.3 two-seat night-fighter versions. Power was provided by the de Havilland Ghost turbojet, giving the FB.Mk.1 a maximum speed of 1030km/h (640mph). Fixed armament comprised four 20mm cannon. Nearly 700 were built for the RAF and FB.Mk.50s were built under license in Switzerland. British Venoms were replaced

by Hunters and Javelins.

The Hawker Hunter itself was a beautifully styled swept-wing fighter, powered by a single rear-mounted Avon turbojet. It first flew as a prototype on 20 July 1951, having been evolved via the experimental swept-wing version of the Sea Hawk, known as the P.1052, continuing Sydney Camm's belief that an aircraft should not only fly right but also look right. Even the Hunter's air brake was not allowed to spoil the lines, being fitted beneath the fuselage. Production Hunter F.Mk.1s entered service with the RAF from July 1954, these being powered by 3400kg (7500lb) thrust Avon 104 or 107

Right: the Hawker Hunter F. Mk. 1 entered service with RAF Fighter Command in 1954.

Below: a D.H. Venom FB.Mk.50 of the Swiss air force, which is the last operator of this fighter.

engines, the first F.Mk.1 off the production line having flown on 30 November 1952. Simultaneous production of the Armstrong Whitworth Sapphire Mk 101-powered Hunter F.Mk.2 took place at Armstrong Whitworth, but few were built. Only a single F.Mk.3 was produced by a conversion, and this took the world speed record from the US F-86D Sabre on 7 September 1953 by attaining an average speed of 1171km/h (727mph).

The Hunter F.Mk.4 was basically an improved F.Mk.1, powered by the Avon 115 on most aircraft. It also introduced underwing attachment points for drop-tanks or weapons to supplement the four 30mm Aden cannon. The Sapphire-powered F.Mk.5 was structurally improved, as was the F.Mk.4, while the more-powerful F.Mk.6 had the 4536kg (10,000lb) thrust Avon 203 engine. Later production F.Mk 6s.had extended leading-edge panels and the option of four underwing stores pylons. It entered

RAF service in 1956, becoming the standard RAF day fighter in Europe.

Of the 1985 Hunters built, many were two-seat trainers and F(GA) ground-attack variants. Production included Hunters built under license in Holland and Belgium, with others being exported to 14 countries in new or refurbished form. Today Hunters in service include 140 F.Mk.58 fighter-bombers operated by Switzerland. Maximum speed of the F.Mk.4 was Mach 0.9, making it undoubtedly the ultimate development of the subsonic fighter.

Hawker later became responsible for the lightweight British Gnat, a Mach 0.98 fighter armed with two cannon (plus rockets or bombs) developed by Folland Aircraft. It first flew on 18 July 1955. Production single-seaters, powered by one 2050kg (4520lb) thrust Bristol Siddeley Orpheus 701 turbojet

Below: a Folland Gnat lightweight fighter in service with the Finnish air force.

Below: a Hawker Hunter F(GA).Mk.9 ground attack fighter of No 45 Squadron, Royal Air Force.

each, were not used by the RAF but were exported to Finland, India and Yugoslavia in small numbers. However the two-seat training variant later became well known to aviation enthusiasts all round the world as the mount of the RAF Red Arrows aerobatic team. A version of the Gnat has also been in production in India since about 1976 as the Ajeet (Invincible) interceptor and ground attack aircraft, as well as in two-seat training form, with 50 single-seaters built by HAL (Hindustan Aeronautics Ltd) by 1981.

Probably the least successful jet fighter produced in Britain for the RAF was the Supermarine Swift, which first flew as an Avon-powered prototype in August 1951. A contemporary of the Hunter, small numbers entered RAF service from 1953 to become that force's first swept-wing fighter, each armed with two or four 30mm cannon, but

Above: the Gloster Javelin F(AW).Mk.1 was the first RAF aircraft to be designed as an all-weather fighter.

Below: the first prototype Gloster Javelin was flown with the second cockpit covered over.

Right: the English Electric P.1A was developed into the Lightning by way of the P.1B.

were withdrawn during 1955. Only the Swift FR.Mk.5 fighter-reconnaissance version was successful, 60 serving between 1956 and 1961. The later Swift F.Mk.7 was used only in very small numbers as a test-bed for missiles.

Gloster Aircraft's only other successful production jet fighter after the Meteor was the Javelin, which was the world's first twin-engined delta-winged aircraft and the RAF's first purpose-designed all-weather fighter. The first of five prototypes flew on 26 November 1951 and RAF Fighter Command began operating production F(AW).Mk.1s in 1956. This first version was powered by two 3765kg (8300lb) thrust Sapphire ASSa.6 turbojets and carried four 30mm Aden guns. Like all nine versions of the Javelin, the F(AW).Mk.1 was a two-seater. Later versions were the F(AW).Mk.2, with an American-designed radar and equipment changes (first flown on 31 October 1955); the F(AW).Mk.4, with an all-moving horizontal tail (first flown 19 Sep-

**Above: the Supermarine Swift F.Mk.7
was used to develop the Fairey Fireflash
air-to-air missile.**

tember 1955); the F(AW).Mk.5, with redesigned wings carrying more fuel (first flown 26 July 1956); the F(AW).Mk.6, with American radar (first flown 14 December 1956); the F(AW).Mk.7, major production version with Sapphire ASSa.7 engines, rated at 4990kg (11,000lb) thrust, airframe modifications, and the ability to carry four Firestreak air-to-air missiles and two guns (first flown 27 April 1956); and the final F(AW).Mk.8, with missiles, guns and afterburning engines (first flown 9 May 1958). In addition, most of the F(AW).Mk.7s were later modified to have afterburning and flight refuelling as Mk.9s. The last of about 400 Javelins were retired in 1967. Maximum speed of the F(AW).Mk.9 was 998km/h (620mph).

The final fighter in this chapter is, like several of the others, still in first-line use today. It is the BAC Lightning, originally the

English Electric Lightning. On 4 August 1954 the first of two English Electric P.1A flying prototypes took off, powered by two Sapphire engines. Designed to an Air Ministry specification for a manned supersonic research aircraft, it had its engines rearmounted one above the other, fed with air from a very large nose intake. From the P.1A was developed the refined P.1B. Like the earlier aircraft it had heavily-swept wings, but power was now provided by afterburning Avon turbojets. Also, the air

Left: an RAF BAC Lightning F.Mk.6 formates on a Handley Page Victor tanker aircraft.

Below: the Royal Saudi Air Force operates a version of the Lightning with ground attack capability.

intake featured a center-body or shock-cone. A P.1B first flew on 4 April 1957 and was the prototype to the Lightning F.Mk 1 and F.Mk 1A, powered by Avon 201s. Forty-eight Mk 1 types were built, able to launch Firestreak missiles, none of which remain in use. The use of Avon 210 engines with improved afterburners and the provision for Firestreak or Red Top missiles (in addition to the 30mm Aden guns) gave rise to the F.Mk 2 and modified 2A, neither of which remain in use.

The F.Mk 3 and 3A were provided with 7420kg (16360lb) thrust Avon 301 engines, missile armament only, redesigned vertical tails with angular tops, and reduced outer wing panel sweep (F.Mk 3A only). The RAF retains 19 today. Other than side-by-side two-seat trainers, the RAF received one more version only, as the F.Mk 6. First flown

in 1964, this version is basically a developed F.Mk 3 with increased fuel capacity. Armament comprise two missiles or two rocket packs, plus two 30mm Aden guns optionally. Most of the F.Mk 3/3As were converted to this standard. The RAF currently operates 40 F.Mk 6s, plus trainers. Two RAF squadrons operate Lightnings as home defense fighters, although Phantom IIs have recently taken over the major share of this role. Nevertheless the Lightning remains one of the fastest climbing fighters in the world, and has a maximum speed of more than Mach 2. But its high performance was not enough to win major export orders. Development had taken too long for this. Only Kuwait and Saudi Arabia purchased new and ex-RAF Lightnings, the Royal Saudi Air Force still operating 30 fighters and seven trainers in the 1980s.

7: INTO THE '80s

Many of the fighters covered in chapters five and six remain in use today. Some are even in production. But this chapter contains the fastest, highest climbing and most potent fighters ever built, as well as those of lesser ability. Interestingly the fastest military aircraft in service today is not a fighter but the Lockheed SR-71A strategic reconnaissance aircraft. Three of the original prototypes of the SR-71A were modified into experimental Mach 3 plus interceptors, being evaluated in 1964.

In the early 1980s the majority of fighters and fighter-bombers in USAF service were two-seat McDonnell Douglas F-4 Phantom IIs, the naval counterparts having already been described in chapter five. A total of more than 1700 was then listed. USAF interest in the Phantom II came about when trials in 1961 proved the aircraft to be well suited to ground attack in addition to fighter duties. The USAF's Tactical Air Command, Pacific Air Forces and United States Air Forces in Europe received the F-4C, which was based on the Navy/USMC F-4B, and powered by two General Electric J79-GE-15 turbojets. Some were later modified into

EF-4Cs, a version developed to carry ECM sensors and anti-radiation missiles to attack antiaircraft radar sites. Other so-called 'Wild Weasel' versions have included the EF-4D and F-4G Advanced Wild Weasel.

The USAF's F-4D was basically similar to the F-4C, but with improved avionics, while the F-4E provided multi-role capability. Delivered from October 1968, the 'E' has 8120kg (17,900lb) thrust J79-GE-17 engines, increased fuel capacity, and carries a fixed 20mm multi-barrel gun. Under MAP, F-4Es also went to Germany, Greece, Iran, Israel, Japan, South Korea, and Turkey. Others now

Overleaf: a General Dynamics F-16A Fighting Falcon.

Far left: the Lockheed YF-12A Mach 3 interceptor did not go into production.

Left: the 5000th Phantom built in the United States was an F-4E, which was delivered to Turkey.

Below: the McDonnell Douglas F-4E was the first variant of the Phantom to have built-in gun armament.

serve also with Australia and Egypt. In addition Mitsubishi of Japan has built 127 under license for the JASDF as F-4EJs, capable of carrying Mitsubishi AAM-2 missiles.

The F-4F fighter was produced for the German Luftwaffe, while the F-4M was the RAF version, a Rolls-Royce Spey-powered variant similar to the Royal Navy F-4K and also capable of carrying Sky Flash air-to-air missiles. The RAF received 118 from 1968. All Phantom II land-based versions remain operational today, except for the EF-4D, which can be regarded as a prototype version for the F-4G. Maximum speed of the F-4E is more than Mach 2, and air-to-air armament comprises the gun plus Sparrow or Sidewinder missiles.

The latest USAF fighter from McDonnell Douglas is the F-15 Eagle. Certainly one of the finest air superiority fighters in the world, it still retains ground attack capability. The single-seat F-15A Eagle was first flown on 27 July 1972, followed by the F-15B two-seat trainer on 7 July 1973. Unlike the contemporary US Navy Tomcat, the Eagle has fixed wings, but shares the relatively new concept of having twin fins and rudders. Powered by two 10,854kg (23,930lb) thrust (with afterburning) Pratt & Whitney F100-PW-100 turbofan engines, it has a maximum speed of more than Mach 2.5. Armament in the air superiority role comprises a 20mm multi-barrel gun plus four Sidewinders and four Sparrows.

By early 1981 600 Eagles had been delivered, those from mid-1979 as F-15Cs and F-15Ds (single and two-seaters respectively) to acknowledge the latest increase in fuel capacity and ability to carry low-drag external fuel and sensor pallets known as FAST Packs. The Packs attach to the sides of the air intakes and so do not detract from the aircraft's streamlining. The USAF plans

to receive 749 Eagles by 1983, while Israel has acquired 25 of an expected total of 40, Japan has received 14 from the United States and plans to build a further 86 under license as F-15Js and F-15DJs and deliveries of 60 Eagles to Saudi Arabia has begun. The name Strike Eagle refers to a specially developed ground attack version.

In an attempt to acquire a low-cost and lightweight supersonic fighter, mainly for overseas use under MAP, the US Department of Defense funded the production of the Northrop F-5A single-seat tactical fighter and two-seat operational F-5B, plus a photographic reconnaissance version. Many air forces received these under MAP or by purchase from the early 1960s. The F-5A attains a speed of 1488km/h (925mph) on the power of two 1850kg (4080lb) thrust (with afterburning) General Electric J85-GE-13 turbojets. Armament comprises two 20mm guns and two Sidewinders, plus underfuselage and underwing stores.

Northrop developed the F-5E and F-5F Tiger II to succeed the F-5A and F-5B. Increased maneuverability was the main aim for the Tiger II, whilst the two 2268kg (5000lb) thrust (with afterburning) J85-GE-21A turbojets allow a speed of Mach 1.63 for the single-seater and slightly less for the two-seat F-5F. Delivery of a very small

Above: a Northrop F-5E tactical fighter carries the markings of the Brazilian Air Force.

Below: a Northrop F-5B leads an echelon formation of F-5As in Royal Norwegian Air Force markings.

number to the USAF for combat training began in early 1973 and by mid-1981 more than 1100 had been delivered to various air forces.

Light weight is also one of the advantages of the General Dynamics F-16 Fighting Falcon, one of the latest US fighters. The first prototype flew on 2 February 1974 and eventually the F-16 was selected for USAF service after competition against the Northrop YF-17. The USAF has stated a requirement for 1388 F-16s, mostly single-seat F-16As but including more than 200 two-seat F-16B fighter-trainers. Power is provided by one 11,340kg (25,000lb) thrust (with afterburning) Pratt & Whitney F100-

PW-200 turbofan engine, giving the F-16A a maximum speed of more than Mach 2. Armament comprises a 20mm multi-barrel gun, two Sidewinders carried at the wing-tips and other weapons carried on seven hardpoints.

In 1975 Belgium, Denmark, the Netherlands and Norway each decided to replace its F-104 Starfighters with F-16s. Deliveries began to Belgium in 1979. Other export Fighting Falcons were ordered by Israel, South Korea and Egypt. Israel received its first fighters in early 1980, and these were used in action in mid-1981 against Iraq's nuclear reactor at Osirak.

The fighters with variable-geometry

Below: a formation of F-16A Fighting Falcons of the 388th Tactical Fighter Wing, the first USAF F-16 unit.

('swing') wings that appeared during the 1970s and are now operational in large numbers or are about to become so, owe their lineage in part to the unique work carried out by General Dynamics for its F-111. This two-seat Mach 2.5 tactical strike fighter was developed for participation in the USAF's Tactical Fighter Experimental (TFX) com-

Left: an F-16B of the Israeli Air Force, which has used the Fighting Falcon in combat.

Right: F-16B two-seaters destined for the air forces of Denmark, the Netherlands, Belgium and Norway.

petition. The winner was intended to be a modern replacement for the Century Series, while also being suitable for operations from aircraft carriers, a role no doubt seen as reasonable following the F-4's compatibility to both land and sea.

Development of the swing-wings took considerable time and effort, but on 6 January 1965 the prototype F-111 varied the sweep of its wings in flight for the first time. Powered by two 8391kg (18,500lb) thrust (with afterburning) Pratt & Whitney TF30-P-1 or P-3 engines, the first production version was the USAF's F-111A, of which 141 were built. The Navy's expected F-111B was cancelled after five development and two production examples had been built. However the 'A' became basically an all-weather bomber in service from 1967. F-111C was the designation given to a version for the Royal Australian Air Force, which received 24, while Britain cancelled its expected F-111Ks. Later USAF versions have included the F-111D with improved avionics and TF30-P-9 turbofan engines, the F-111E with modified air intakes and the F-111F. Of 296 D/E/Fs built, 106 were F-111F fighter-bombers with 11,385kg (25,100lb) thrust (with afterburning) TF30-P-100 turbofans, capable of Mach 2.5 performance. Armament comprises a 20mm multi-barrel can-

Right: the USAF's General Dynamics F-111F is a low-level bomber with terrain-following capability.

Below: a prototype of the RAF's Panavia Tornado F.Mk.2, which is the Tornado air defense variant.

Above: 90 BAe Hawk T.Mk.1 jet trainers are being adapted to carry AIM-9L Sidewinders in the air defense role.

Right: the Mikoyan MiG-25 *Foxbat* is the world's fastest combat aircraft in current service.

non, plus underwing stores and bombs in the weapon bay. The first F-111Es arrived in Britain in 1970, followed by other aircraft.

Britain's own swing-wing combat plane is the Panavia Tornado, which it shares with Germany and Italy. Most of the 809 Tornados to be built for the three countries will be attack versions, but the RAF is to receive 165 Tornado ADVs (air defence variant) as Tornado F.Mk 2s, each armed with a 27mm IWKA-Mauser cannon plus four Sky Flash and two Sidewinder missiles. The two-seater is powered by two 7257kg (16,000lb) thrust (with afterburning) Turbo-Union RB.199-34R-04 turbofan engines, giving it a maximum speed of more than Mach 2. The first Tornado ADV prototype flew on 27 October 1979 and production aircraft will appear in 1983.

All of the more recent Soviet interceptors and fighter-bombers have swing-wings, with the exceptions of the Sukhoi Su-15 (NATO *Flagon*), a twin-turbojet and delta-winged Mach 2.3 single-seat interceptor, of which about 700 are operational, and the Mikoyan MiG-25 (NATO *Foxbat A*). The lat-

ter is the single-seat interceptor version of the MiG-25, powered by two 11,000kg (24,251lb) thrust (with afterburning) Tumansky R-31 turbojet engines. It carries four air-to-air missiles of *Acrid, Aphid* or *Apex* type, and has a maximum speed with missiles of Mach 2.8 (probably Mach 3.2 without missiles), making it the fastest combat aircraft in the world. Well over 300 are believed to be in use as interceptors with the Soviet air force.

The Sukhoi Su-17 (NATO *Fitter*) is basically a ground attack fighter, powered by two 11,200kg (24,692lb) thrust (with afterburning) Lyulka AL-21F-3 turbojet engines, as is the Su-20 export version and simplified export Su-22. the Sukhoi Su-24 (NATO *Fencer*) is, like the others, a variable-geometry aircraft, but for attack only.

The MiG-23 (NATO *Flogger*) has a ground attack counterpart in the MiG-27, but is itself a single-seat variable-geometry fighter. It has been built in several versions for Soviet use and export since the early 1970s and it is estimated that approximately 2000 MiG-23/27s have gone into Soviet service, with production continuing at several hundred a year. The MiG-23 is one type gradually replacing the Sukhoi Su-15.

Powered by a single 12,500kg (27,558lb) thrust Tumansky R-29B turbojet, the MiG-23MF (*Flogger-B*) is now the most important Soviet tactical fighter, displacing the MiG-21. It has a maximum speed of Mach 2.3 and is armed with one 23mm GSh-23 gun plus *Apex* or *Aphid* missiles or other weapons carried on five hardpoints.

France also developed a variable-geometry fighter as the Mirage G8, but this remained a prototype. Some years earlier Dassault moved away temporarily from its

standard delta and vertical tail configuration by developing its Mirage F1, a single-seat multi-mission fighter and ground attack aircraft with swept wings and a conventional swept tail unit. The prototype first flew on 23 December 1966 but production F1-Cs did not enter French air force service until 1973. Powered by a 7,200kg (15,873lb) thrust (with afterburning) turbojet engine, the F1-C has a maximum speed of Mach 2.2. It carries two 30mm DEFA cannon plus three Matra R 530 or Super 530 and two Sidewinder or Matra 550 Magic air-to-air

missiles as an interceptor. Twenty-five F1-Cs have recently been given flight refuelling capability as F1-C-200s. The only other fighter version of the F1 is the F1-E, with improved avionics. By 1981 nearly 400 F1s had been built, including many for export.

The very latest French fighters are the Mirage 2000 and the Super Mirage 4000, both returning to Dassault's trusted delta wing form. The former is basically a single-seat interceptor and air superiority fighter, powered by a SNECMA M53 turbofan engine. The first prototype flew on 10

Above: a Sukhoi Su-20 ground-attack fighter is pictured in service with the Egyptian air force.

Left: the Mikoyan MiG-23 *Flogger* is the Soviet Union's most important tactical fighter aircraft.

Right: a French Mirage F1 is armed with ground attack weapons. It also serves as an interceptor aircraft.

Above left: a two-seat Mirage G8 formates on a single-seat version of this variable-geometry fighter.

Above: a Dassault Mirage F1-E interceptor carries wingtip-mounted air-to-air missiles.

Left: Mirage F1 fighters (foreground) pictured on the production line shortly before rollout.

Right: three Mirage 2000 prototypes fly in formation with the larger, twin-engined Super Mirage 4000.

March 1978 and delivery of the first single-seaters and two-seat trainers will begin in 1983. Typical armament will comprise two 30mm DEFA cannon plus two Super 530 and two Magic missiles. A prototype two-seat low-level penetration version of the Mirage 2000 will fly in 1983 as the Mirage 2000N.

A considerably larger aircraft is the Super Mirage 4000, first flown on 9 March 1979. Powered by two M53 engines, it too is a single-seater but is designated a multi-role combat type. It is likely that this aircraft has a maximum speed similar to the Mirage 2000's Mach 2.2.

In September 1969 Israel flew the prototype of an indigenous fighter based on the French Mirage III/5. This became the Nesher, about 40 of which entered Israeli service from 1972. From the Nesher IAI developed the Kfir-C1, which flew in prototype form in 1973. This delta-winged fighter is powered by an 8,120kg (17,902lb) thrust (with afterburning) General Electric J79-J1E turbojet engine and possesses a maximum speed of more than Mach 2.

From the Kfir-C1 was developed the Kfir-C2, the most obvious external difference being the use of small canards. This improved Kfir entered service during the mid-1970s. Earlier-built Kfirs are being updated to C2 standard, in which form maneuverability and take off/landing performance is improved. About 200 Kfirs have been built, each armed with two 30mm cannon and two Shafrir air-to-air missiles or ground attack weapons.

Saab's most recent interceptor for the Swedish air force is the JA 37 Viggen, just one of five versions of the Saab-37 that have been built. The Viggen first flew as a prototype on 8 February 1967, production eventually starting with the AJ 37 single-seat attack variant. The single-seat JA 37 has been delivered as a Draken replacement since 1979, but this too has attack capability. The Swedish air force expects to receive 149 JA 37s by 1985, each powered by a single 12,750kg (28,100lb) thrust (with after-

Left: Israel Aircraft Industries developed the Kfir-C1 fighter from the French Dassault Mirage III/5.

Above: the IAI Kfir-C2 is fitted with small canard foreplanes, which enhance maneuverability.

burning) Volvo Flygmotor RM8B turbofan engine, bestowing a maximum speed of Mach 2 plus. Easily recognizable by its tandem delta-type wings and canards, the JA 37 can be armed with one 30mm Oerlikon cannon and six Sky Flash and Sidewinder missiles.

India became one of the select band of countries to develop and produce a supersonic fighter in May 1964, when the Indian Air Force took delivery of its first HAL HF-24 Marut attack fighters. Powered by two 2200kg (4850lb) thrust HAL-built Rolls-Royce Bristol Orpheus 703 turbojet engines, allowing a maximum speed of 1,112km/h (691mph), the single-seat Maruts can each carry four 30mm Aden guns and an under-fuselage retractable pack of fifty SNEB 68mm air-to-air rockets, plus ground attack weapons under the wings.

Japan also joined the select band when Mitsubishi produced its F-1. This was developed as a close-support fighter from the earlier T-2 two-seat trainer, the first prototype flying on 3 June 1975. Production aircraft have been delivered to the JASDF since September 1977 and by early 1981 deliveries amounted to 57 of the 67 so far ordered. Each F-1 is powered by two 3207kg (7070lb) thrust (with afterburning) Japanese-built Adour turbofan engines, known as TF40-IHI-801As, giving a Mach 1.6 performance. Armament comprises one 20mm JM61 multi-barrel cannon plus four Sidewinders or ground attack weapons.

Romania and Yugoslavia joined forces to produce their first supersonic combat plane, a single-seat tactical fighter known as the CNIAR IAR-93 and SOKO Orao respectively. First flown as a prototype on 31 October 1974, the production version is powered by two 2270kg (5000lb) thrust (with afterburning) Rolls-Royce Viper Mk

Above: a Saab JA 37 Viggen interceptor is pictured carrying Sidewinder and Sky Flash air-to-air missiles.

Left: Viggen pilots of the Swedish air force's F 13 Wing pose on the flightline in front of their aircraft.

632 turbojet engines and can achieve a speed of 1130km/h (702mph). Each nation is expected to receive about 200 aircraft, including two-seat training examples, each armed with two 23mm cannon.

Development of jet fighters never stops. As one new fighter enters production so another leaves the drawing board: a pattern of events repeated in many countries.

In the United States, General Dynamics is developing an advanced version of its F-16 and Northrop a version of its F-5 as the F-5G Tigershark, while in the Soviet Union Mikoyan is reportedly flight testing a new Mach 2 plus fighter roughly equivalent to the US Hornet. In China the Mach 2 plus Shenyang J-8 is under development, while designs for lightweight multi-role types have appeared in Sweden and Switzerland, as the JAS/Saab 2105 and ALR Piranha respectively, both of these with rear-mounted main wings and canards. The jet fighter story has no immediate end, just a point at which no further information is available!

BOMBERS

Previous pages: The Rockwell B-1 supersonic
US bomber in flight.
Below: Two Grumman F-14A Tomcat fighters
on the US Navy's VF-213.

8: A FLASH OF LIGHTNING

oward the end of World War II a typical heavy bomber carried perhaps 6350kg (14,000lb) of bombs at a speed usually not exceeding 480km/h (300mph). It was not uncommon for about 1000 bombers of various types to be used on a single raid, leaving massive devastation as never seen before and climaxed only by the atomic bombs dropped on Hiroshima and Nagasaki in August 1945. Yet in the 1980s a single-seat, lightweight air combat fighter of General Dynamics F-16 Fighting Falcon caliber can itself carry a warload of up to 9276kg (20,450lb) in a secondary attack role. To confuse issues further, Fairchild Republic A-10A Thunderbolt II close-support aircraft in service with the USAF are deployed by what are called Tactical Fighter Wings, yet the A-10 has provision for virtually every form of ground attack weapon but no air-to-air armament.

The meaning of the term 'bomber' has become confused over the years and nowadays is often used only when referring to strategic bombers deployed to deliver an attack on selected targets within the enemy's territory. However, it can be assumed that there are two other categories of 'bomber' before encompassing multi-role combat aircraft of primary fighter design and fighter-bombers. These are tactical bombers and attack aircraft. Tactical operations are against opposing enemy forces within a limited area, and this can be within or outside the territory of the attacked or the aggressor. Attack is more general and can also cover other terms such as ground support and interdiction. It is normally accepted to mean a mission against a specific tactical surface target or on a target behind enemy lines. It is within the framework of strategic, tactical and attack that this book is based, stopping short of heavily-laden air combat fighters and fighter-bombers.

It is a curious fact, or perhaps more correctly a financial dictate, that the world's air forces have fewer strategic bombers in service today than at any time since World War I. It is true that the awsome capabilities of modern aircraft coupled with the incredible destructive power of the latest missiles and bombs make individual bombers of today far more formidable than a squadron from past decades, yet this is not the whole picture. The Royal Air Force, for example, with a tradition of strategic bombing capability

that originated as long ago as 1917 with the formation of the 41st Wing (then correctly part of the Royal Flying Corps) to bomb strategic industrial targets in Germany, is on the verge of having no bomber capable of a long-range strategic mission. Yet it was the Vulcan, earmarked for the scrapyard, that was instantly reprieved for service in the South Atlantic in 1982. Similarly, NATO as a whole relies on the USAF's ageing Boeing B-52 Stratofortress as its only heavy long-range bomber, its capabilities continuously enhanced by the addition of advanced systems and new missiles. The Soviet Union, with its own tradition of a large strategic bomber force dating from the 1920s, is the only nation currently developing and deploying strategic bombers as part of a continuous program.

It is a matter of history that the last sortie over Britain by the Luftwaffe during World War II was flown by an Arado Ar 234B Blitz (Lightning) reconnaissance aircraft from KG 76. The Blitz, however, is best remembered as the world's first turbojet-powered bomber in its Ar 234B-2 version and Germany's second jet in military service.

It all began on 27 August 1939 when Germany flew the first ever turbojet-powered airplane, the diminutive Heinkel He 178. In fact virtually all of the credit for achieving this honor was due to just two men, Ernst Heinkel, head of the aircraft manufacturing company bearing his name, and Hans Joachim Pabst von Ohain who conceived the engine upon which it flew. But in 1937 Junkers had begun development of its own turbojet engine, encouraged by the technical division of the Reichsluftfahrtministerium (RLM), the German aviation ministry. The outcome was the Jumo 109-004, first started up in November 1940. Despite Heinkel's early lead with turbojet engines, it was upon the Junkers turbojet and the favored rival, the BMW 109-003 which also first ran in 1940, that the RLM based a 1940 specification for a twin-engined high-speed reconnaissance aircraft. It is fact, therefore, that in the year before Britain flew its first turbojet-powered aircraft, Germany actually planned operational types.

During the next months Dipl Ing Walter Blume and Ing Hans Rebeski of the Arado Flugzeugwerke GmbH made several preliminary design studies for the aircraft,

which was expected to fly into enemy airspace with impunity by virtue of a high operating altitude coupled with high speed. And who could fault the logic. Since the latter half of 1940 specially-prepared

A General Dynamics F-16A Fighting Falcon dropping a bombload similar in weight to that carried by many heavy bombers of World War II.

Previous page: Captured Arado Ar 234B Blitz in Allied markings.

Junkers Ju 86P high-flying reconnaissance aircraft, with pressurized cabins for the crews, had flown missions over Britain without interception.

In early 1941 proposal E.370 was accepted by the RLM and the Arado Ar 234, later named Blitz (Lightning), germinated. In fact the airframe was conventional considering the pioneering concept. The turbojet engines were carried beneath the high-mounted (often quoted as shoulder-mounted) tapering wings, which had flush riveted stressed skins. Very narrow-chord Frise-type ailerons with mass-balanced geared tabs were fitted on the inboard sec-

tions, and hydraulically-actuated flaps were positioned each side of the turbojet nacelles. The semi-monocoque circular-section fuselage also had flush-riveted stressed skins, and it was the narrowness of this, coupled with wing position, that gave rise to the aircraft's most unusual feature.

It is probably true to say that the Ar 234 owed some of its design features to the Ar 232, a general-purpose transport conceived to a 1939 specification. This had the pilot's cockpit in the extreme nose of the fuselage (although in the Ar 234's case the cockpit was expected to be pressurized), high-mounted wings, and a unique undercarriage arrangement that included eleven pairs of small wheels in tandem under the fuselage, a large nosewheel and long legs for the mainwheels under the engines. This rather strange arrangement resulted from the need to produce a strong undercarriage, but one which was sufficiently low to allow freight to be loaded directly from trucks and which would not restrict freight-carrying room inside the fuselage when the main wheels were retracted. The Ar 234 presented the designers with similar problems, as a retractable undercarriage had to be devised that would not be effected by the narrowness of the fuselage nor the height or thinness of the wings. There appeared but few solutions. One, which must have been inspired by the Ar 232, was to adopt a large number of small retractable wheels in tandem beneath the fuselage and stabilizing skids on outriggers beneath the engine nacelles and retracting into them. In the event, the RLM decided upon the concept of using a jettisonable take-off trolley, leaving the aircraft to land on an underfuselage main skid and the under-nacelle skids. Interestingly, this system of take-off and landing was not unique to the Blitz and even found favor after the war in France when that country developed an experimental tactical fighter that could operate independently of airfields with long runways.

In operation, the Ar. 234 was to be mounted on a non-powered tricycle trolley, which had a steerable nosewheel and pilot-operated brakes. At the moment of lift off, the trolley was to jettison, a braking parachute stopping it from careering to destruction and so allowing reuse. Apart from the obvious restrictions of airfield clearance once Ar 234s had landed, as the stranded aircraft would need to be lifted and towed away, this system appeared to be the answer, especially as it gave the added bonus of reducing the aircraft's all-up weight.

V13 configured as an Ar 234C-type prototype with paired engines.

Prototype construction began in early 1941 but a cruel blow lay in store. By late 1941 the first prototypes were nearing completion but there had been no delivery of engines to power them. Indeed, the Junkers Jumo 109-004 development program was well behind schedule and Messerschmitt had priority for delivery of early 004s from the factory for its fighter. Further, BMW was obtaining thrust ratings well below those expected from its 109-003 turbojet. In reality, by this time the Jumo 109-004 had only just been flown experimentally by a Messerschmitt Bf 110 and modifications were then in hand to produce the improved 004B as a follow-up engine to the initial 004A.

Although Messerschmitt was in the same boat when it came to prepared airframes for its first jet aircraft but no engines, at least that company had managed to get its Me 262 off the ground on the power of a nose-mounted piston engine. The Ar 234 was unable to do this, as the skids on which it would land provided too little ground clearance for propellers. Arado was forced to recognize that flight testing could not begin until Jumo 109-004As arrived.

Hopeful signs came in July 1942, when a prototype Me 262 was flown on the power of Jumo 109-004As. Surely Arado need not wait much longer. In fact Arado had to wait another seven months for a delivery from Junkers and, as fighters and fighter-bombers had priority, the only two engines then received were not cleared for flight. At least ground testing could now begin and with these installed Ar 234 V1 undertook taxying trials using the trolley arrangement. Progress was now rapid. Two months later, in May, this aircraft was sent to Rheine airfield where two new flight-cleared Junkers turbojets were installed. So as not to take any chances with the prototype, it was decided that the take-off trolley should not be jettisoned at lift-off but carried to an altitude of approximately 60m (195ft), at which height it would be released to descend on parachutes.

On 15 June 1943, almost eleven months after an Me 262 prototype had flown on 004As, the first Ar 234 prototype took to the air with Flugkapitän Selle in the pilot's seat. Later in the development program Selle was to lose his life in V7, but this first flight proved a tremendous success. The only problem was the destruction of the trolley, which had been jettisoned on schedule but had dropped like a stone to the ground without its parachutes deployed. After a second trolley was lost in a similar way, flight testing reverted to jettisoning at take-off.

A total of seven prototypes was completed, the third being the first preproduction standard example with cabin pressurization and an ejection seat for the pilot, and three inset lugs outboard of the engine nacelles for attaching RATOG (rocket assisted take-off gear). Meanwhile, it had

been decided to increase the aircraft's land mobility by abandoning the trolley take-off system and adopting a newly-designed nosewheel gear. Each unit of the new gear was fitted with a large low-pressure tire, the nosewheel retracting into a compartment to the rear of the cockpit and the main units retracting forward and inward into a wider fuselage. The result of this arrangement was to give the undercarriage a very narrow track. By virtue of the modifications, the 'A' series Ar 234 was abandoned in favor of the Ar 234B.

For series production of the Ar 234B, assembly lines were established at Alt Lönnewitz. Some reports that appeared in Britain soon after the end of the war suggested that the first Ar 234B flew in December 1943. This is incorrect. The first of only three Ar 234B prototypes to fly before the first of twenty preproduction Ar 234B-Os, on 8 June 1944, was Ar 234 V9, which flew on 10 March 1944. It must be assumed, therefore, that the early reports mistook the Ar 234 V5 as a series 'B' type. This aircraft, which indeed flew on 20 December 1943, was the first to have the lightened 840kg (1852lb) thrust Jumo 109-004B-0 turbojets installed. In other respects V5 was a true 'A' series aircraft, but might have confused matters further by lacking a pressurized cabin for the pilot, a feature common to the Ar 234B-Os. Ejection seats were also deleted from Ar 234B-Os.

Ar 234B-Os were completed with provision for two reconnaissance cameras each, with a choice of two Rb 75/30s, two Rb 50/ 30s, or one Rb 20/30 and one Rb 75/30. Of the twenty, the statutory thirteen were delivered to the flight-proving center at Rechlin, where they were used for evaluation purposes. Meanwhile, V5 and V7 had undertaken the first actual operations, with 1 Staffel/Versuchsverband Ob d L, the first on 20 July from an airfield at Juvincourt only ten days after KG 51 Kommando Schenk had arrived there with its Me 262s. By the following September the unit had moved twice and was then to be found at Rheine, where two Ar 234B-Os joined the single remaining prototype. Within a short time full production Ar 234B-1 reconnaissance aircraft began to appear, allowing the formation of the first operational unit proper as Sonderkommando Götz, although this unit drew only partial strength from the previous evaluation Staffel. By November two more special Arado units were forming. Operation of the three special units lasted only a short time, giving way in January 1945 to three newly-formed squadrons based at Rheine and in Denmark.

The Ar 234B-1 was purely a reconnaissance aircraft, as originally specified, but had provision for drop tanks to increase the operating radius. Again some reports that appeared in Britain after the war suggested that provision was made for each B-1 to carry two rear-firing 20mm MG 151 cannon with 200 rounds of ammunition per gun. It is not clear how many, if indeed any, actually carried defensive armament, especially in view of the fact that the Blitz was expected to have a performance sufficiently high to make interception very unlikely. Then to be considered is the detrimental effect the weight of cannon and ammunition would have on overall speed and range. Many of the operational photographic reconnaissance missions were over British airfields and harbors and these were not generally troubled by defending fighter planes. Operating altitude for the Blitz was normally about 9000m (29,500ft).

From the outset it had been recognized that the Ar 234B-1 could be superseded by an improved B-2 model, which itself could have several sub-variants to include combat types. Certainly the Blitz had the performance to make it a devastating offensive weapon. It was therefore only a matter of time before the B-2 was in hand for photographic reconnaissance, pathfinding and bombing roles. Each Ar 234B-2 had a tail parachute stowed in the rear fuselage for braking to reduce landing distance, the same 20mm cannon defensive armament as mentioned previously, and Patin PDS three-axis autopilot to allow the single crew member to use the Lotfe 7K bombsight. Various bomb combinations were possible, including the carriage of one 1000kg bomb under the fuselage and one 500kg bomb under each engine nacelle, although a total warload of 1000kg was fairly normal. Maximum speed of the Ar 234B-2 was 742km/h (461mph) at 6000m (19,680ft), but this could be reduced by as much as 97km/h (60mph) when carrying a full warload. Normal take-off weight was 8400kg (18,520lb), although 8850kg (19,510lb) was the maximum permissible take-off weight without rocket assistance and 9800kg (21,605lb) with RATOG. Service ceiling was approximately 10,000m (32,800ft), but altitudes in excess of 11,500m (37,730ft) were obtainable. Range was up to 1630km (1,000 miles). Take-off distance with and without RATOG, carrying a 1500kg warload, was 1785m (5,860ft) and 860m (2820ft) respectively.

In October 1944 the first B-2 bombers became available to Kampfgeschwader 76. Pilots were trained to fly these jets on two-seat Messerschmitt Me 262B-la conversion aircraft of IV(Erg)/KG 51 at the factory site. The first Gruppe of this unit flew the first operational missions by a purpose-built jet bomber, flying from Rheine and Achmer to attack Allied targets during the Ardennes offensive which started on 16 December 1944 and continued until 16 January. By then other Gruppe of KG 76 were in training. Between then and the end of the war in Europe, Arado bomber units suffered severe fuel shortages and were moved from one base to another as the situation grew ever more desperate for Germany. Then, on 24 February 1945, an Ar 234B-2 from III Gruppe of KG 76 operating with other B-2s and Me 262 fighter-bombers, lost engine power and was forced down by USAAF piston-engined fighters near Segelsdorf. This Blitz was captured by US ground forces on the following day, the first Ar 234 to be taken in one piece by the Allies. During much of early March KG 76 and accompanying Me 262 fighter-bombers attempted to hold up the Allied crossings of the Rhine. This was undoubtedly the high-point in the career of the Blitz bomber.

Although a small number of new Blitz aircraft were delivered to operational units thereafter, by the beginning of April what remained of KG 76 was grouped at four locations, each with only a handful of aircraft at most. From then on the situation became daily more hopeless and fewer and fewer attacks were mounted. In the forty months that separated the appearance of the first Ar 234 airframes and the end of the war in Europe, fewer than 250 operational Blitz aircraft had been built, most of which were of the 'B' series.

Going back to the spring of 1942, the serious problems BMW were experiencing with its 109-003 turbojet engine were going to take a further year and a half of work to put right before this company too had a viable engine for production. In October 1943, however, BMW demonstrated its redesigned 109-003A in the air. Lighter than the 004, it proved suitable for use in production aircraft, although later series-built 003A-1 engines still had problems to be resolved. The availability of the BMW and the ease at which the Ar 234 had completed early flight trials led to much forward thinking. Beyond the Ar 234B was considered the 'C' type, powered by no less than four BMW turbojets. The RLM's confidence in the Blitz, and to a similar extent the manufacturer's,

was shown clearly by the single act of assigning two of the original Ar 234 prototypes to the development of a 'C' series. Naturally both V6 and V8 had trolley/skid undercarriages, but V6 featured four turbojet engines spaced under the wings and V8 had them in two paired nacelles. The first to fly was V8, on 1 February 1944. It was this configuration that proved the most suitable. Several prototypes for the Ar 234C were flown thereafter, the first prototype proper being V19 with 003A-1 engines and incorporating several design innovations. This aircraft flew on the last day of September 1944. V20 appeared in October and featured a redesigned cockpit with double glazing for pressurization.

Several 'C' series variants were planned, each with the height of the cockpit raised to improve vision and using double-glazed panels, redesigned ailerons, air brakes and an enlarged nosewheel among refinements.

In the event only some nine production Ar 234C-1 single-seat reconnaissance aircraft and five pre-production C-3 combat aircraft were constructed, none of which went into action before Germany's capitulation. Other variants planned included the Ar 234C-4 and C-5 reconnaissance machines, the former with four cannon for defense and the latter a two-seater; C-2, C-5 two-seater and twin Jumo 109-004D-engined C-8 bombers; and the C-7 two-seat night fighter with a choice of engines, including the 003A-1 from BMW and the Heinkel-Hirth 109-011A. The latter was a second-generation turbojet, the work of von Ohain and initially known as the S.11. Intended to have a thrust of 1300kg (2866lb), it had many innovations including a two-position variable exhaust nozzle. Contemporary reports suggest that this was seen as the driving force for a variable-pitch propeller, for use on a future bomber, as projected under the engine

number 021. Actually, the S.11 was the initial stage in the development of the 021, but was put into production towards the end of hostilities.

An enormous number of experimental and prototype S.11s were ordered to speed up development. After some of the second series of engines had been completed, development shifted to the 011A-0 preproduction model. By January 1945 four engines of the second series alone had accumulated more than 180 running hours. Progress with the Ar 234C series was, however, severely disrupted by Allied bombing raids. Maximum speed of the Ar 234C was 874km/h (543mph) at 6000m (19,680ft) and endurance at 60 percent power was approximately 1.25 hours. Several other versions of the Blitz were considered and interesting experiments included the famous Diechselschlepp trials, which involved the Blitz towing a jettisonable long-range fuel tank, or one of various missiles.

Junkers Ju 287 V1 with Walter 501 rocket motors attached below each engine pod.

The Heinkel-Hirth 109-011A engine was also selected as one of the possible powerplants for other projected bombers, the only two to have prototypes put in hand being the Junkers Ju 287 heavy bomber and the diminutive Henschel Hs 132 dive bomber and ground attack jet. The Ju 287 would have been the world's first heavy jet bomber had it achieved operational status.

Development of the Ju 287 started in 1943, when it became known that a new heavy bomber was required for the Luftwaffe as an eventual replacement for the Heinkel He 177 Greif. The Greif had had a particularly troublesome service career up to this date and had earned the nickname 'Flaming Coffin.' The Ju 287 was to be a revolutionary replacement, not only having turbojet engines but incorporating advanced design wings using technical data on swept wings obtained by official research institutes. The main task was to produce a bomber that could outfly all Allied fighters. Of course Junkers had not been the only manufacturer to put pen to paper. Heinkel produced its four-turbojet He 343 design and Blohm und Voss produced several designs for four-jet bombers, each with a unique W-form wing that it was thought would combine the best flying characteristics of forward and swept-back wings. To avoid confusion with other major bomber projects of the period, it should be made clear at this point that of these projected Greif replacements only the Ju 287 continued to prototype construction stage.

In charge of the Junkers Ju 287 project was Dipl Ing Wocke, who recognized the value of swept wings for achieving high speed flight but also saw the dangers they

bestowed for low speed flying. He therefore proposed a wing configuration nearly as strange as that being expounded by Blohm und Voss. Instead of a sweptback wing with a 25 degree sweep, he proposed that the wings of his bomber should be swept forward. Wind tunnel tests showed clearly that whilst low speed flying characteristics were improved over and above sweptback swings, some destabilizing effects resulted at high speed which affected the structure. Nonetheless, the high speed problems were considered less of a worry and work on the bomber prototypes began.

As a first stage, and in order to test the wing configuration at low flying speeds, it was decided to fit newly-built forward swept wings to a readily available fuselage as near to that of the projected bomber as possible. There was only one obvious candidate, and a Greif fuselage received the wings and various component parts from other Junkers aircraft. As a suitable retractable undercarriage was going to be difficult to fit, and was anyway superfluous, a fixed arrangement with large faired wheels under the wings and a twin-wheel nosegear was used. The nosewheels came from the USAAF, having been stripped from a captured B-24 Liberator. The all-important engines were four 900kg (1984lb) Jumo 109-004-B-1s, two in pods under the wings and two mounted either side of the nose. Contemporary reports suggested that the Ju 287 was intended ultimately to use only two new-generation BMW or Junkers turbojets in the 2500-3200kg (5500-7050lb) thrust range. This is interesting and indicates the importance attached to the long-term development of the BMW 109-018 and the Junkers 109-012. The 018 was never completed but would have been a turbojet with a 12-stage axial compressor, a three-stage turbine and a variable exhaust nozzle. Thrust rating was expected to be 3400kg (7496lb). The 012 was in fact the favored engine for the long-term Ju 287 variant, although Germany's capitulation left no time for completion. This smaller engine comprised an 11-stage axial compressor and a two-stage turbine, allowing for a thrust of around 2800kg (6170lb). Interestingly, the BMW engine designation 109-028 applied to a projected variant of the 018, modified to drive contra-rotating propellers. The projected engines apart, actual preproduction and production Ju 287As were to have six BMW 003A-1s each, followed by the initial 'B' series aircraft with four 109-011As.

The resulting misfit was known as the Ju

287 V1 and was a two-seater: the actual Ju 287 was to be a three-seater with accommodation for a pilot in a Ju 288-style raised cockpit, bomb-aimer/navigator and radio operator/gunner for the remotely-controlled tail turret fitted with two 13mm MG 131 machine-guns (Ju 188C style).

With just the four 004B-1s fitted it was

This artist's impression shows how the Ju 287 V2 might have looked if completed in Germany.

clear that the Ju 287 V1 was going to be underpowered, and so it was moved to Brandis for flight trials to make use of the very long runway. The first of 17 flights was recorded on 16 August 1944. Additional power was provided by Walter 501 rocker motors attached to each engine pod and jettisoned after height had been achieved. During the trials the aircraft proved virtually vice-free, although landing speeds were high.

Construction of two actual Ju 287 pro-

The wing position of the Ju 287 V1 is clearly shown from this view.

totypes began thereafter, V3 using the expected production 'A' series layout of four underwing 003A-1s and two nose mounted engines and V2 with three engines in clusters under each wing. However, in the Summer of 1944, when fighter production and development were given the utmost priority in view of the round-the-clock Allied bombing raids on Germany, the Ju 287 was abandoned. Then, in early 1945, despite the ever worsening situation, work restarted on the V2 and V3 at Leipzig, but only V2 reached assembly stage. Soviet forces eventually captured the factory and took V1 and V2 back to the Soviet Union, where V2 was fitted with sweptback wings and flown in 1947. Completion was helped by Junkers staff sent to Podberezhye the previous year. It is difficult to see what was gained by the completion of V2 in the Soviet Union, as by 1947 that nation had its own Tupolev Tu-73 and Tu-77 prototype turbojet-powered bombers flying. The answer must be that this aircraft made convenient engine test-

bed for evaluating captured engines and allowed early research into swept wings.

As for the Henschel Hs 132, this too stopped at three prototypes, all of which were taken over by Soviet forces. However, several interesting points accrue from this project. It is an historical fact that the shortest time to elapse between a contract being issued for a new jet fighter and the first flight of a prototype was the 69 days taken for the small Heinkel He 162. Built in a time of acute strategic material shortages, it used wooden wings and a metal fuselage, the engine being mounted above the fuselage. The simplicity of the He 162, which first flew at the end of 1944, undoubtedly influenced Henschel when it designed its Hs 132 dive-bomber and ground attack jet. This too had a small cigar-shaped fuselage, wooden wings and a dorsal-mounted turbojet. However, because of its role, the pilot lay in a prone position looking through a heavily-glazed forward fuselage. The pilot and structure were expected to withstand a load factor of up to 12g. The maximum designed speed was 792km/h (492mph) at 900m (2950ft) without a bombload. Prototype con-

struction started in March 1945 and at least the first was virtually ready to fly when peace intervened. There is no evidence to suggest that the Hs 132 influenced any post-war Soviet thinking. Nor did the experimental aircraft with prone accommodation for the pilots that appeared in Britain, the United States and elsewhere after the war owe anything to the German machine. Viewed in retrospect, the Hs 132 would probably have been a very simple combat aircraft to construct, but difficult to fly.

May 1945 brought the capitulation of Germany and an end to the war in Europe. It also marked the end of jet bomber development in Germany, for no other jet bomber has been produced in that country since 1945. That country's contribution to aviation history, however, cannot be overstated, introducing as it did the world's first turbojet-powered aircraft, the first turbojet-powered fighter, the first turbojet-powered reconnaissance aircraft, the first turbojet-powered bomber, the first turbojet-powered heavy bomber, and the first turbojet-powered dive-bomber (completed but not flown).

9: BACKING THE BOMBER

The end of World War II saw Germany divided and in ruins. For the remainder of 1945 Britain had the only air force in the world with an operational jet fighter force, but appeared in no hurry to deploy a jet bomber. Having fought hard and long to achieve victory, Britain could not envisage being involved in another major war until at least the 1950s. It was undoubtedly this line of thinking that also delayed the development of a swept-wing fighter in Britain. Another consideration was the practical side of producing a jet bomber using the turbojet engines then available. Although Germany had accepted jet bombers into service with short ranges and light warloads, there appeared no point in rushing the production of a bomber if the end product could not strike hard at long distance targets. No future war was likely to require a bomber with only sufficient range to reach France or Germany. Therefore, it was not until 1949 that the first British jet

Previous page: The Boeing B-47E Stratojet introduced a new 'solid' nose with a refueling probe.

The experimental Douglas XA-26F. Note the air-scoop above the fuselage. Fuel for the turbojet engine was carried in the upper rear section of the bomb-bay.

bomber flew, having been developed at a moderate pace to Specification B.3/45.

Such considerations were not shared by other countries. Both the United States and the Soviet Union accelerated development of jet fighters and bombers, the latter having much ground to make up. The United States was in the happier position, having its own turbojet engines in production and with deliveries of P-80 Shooting Star fighters beginning in late 1945. The mighty resources of the US had been turned to war production after the shattering blow of Pearl Harbor, the legacy of which was not only to make the nation one of the major postwar arms producers, but forced upon it the unenviable role of 'superpower,' for it alone had the atomic bomb.

Development of US jet bombers can be traced back to World War II, although the first purpose-designed jet bomber did not fly until 1946. In October 1941 the General Electric Company received from Britain a Whittle turbojet engine, drawings for the Whittle W2B turbojet and a team of British engineers with a view to establishing a turbojet production line in the US. The Americans equivalent of the W2B became known as the I-A, an experimental engine which powered the Bell P-59 Airacomet. From the I-A General Electric developed the I-16, a 'thirsty,' centrifugal-flow engine which later

The first Douglas XB-43 Mixmaster, with a plywood nosecone fitted in place of the fully-transparent bomb-aiming nose.

received the military designation J31. Apart from becoming the powerplant for the production Airacomet and the tail engine of the Ryan FR-1 Fireball, the Douglas Aircraft Company installed an I-16 in the tail of an A-26 Invader attack bomber as the experimental XA-26F. This installation meant the deletion of turret armament, but was intended to add 56km/h (35mph) to the aircraft's maximum speed. The main engines were two Pratt & Whitney R-2800-83 radials. In the event, hostilities with Japan ended some weeks before the XA-26F was ready for testing, but on 26 June 1946 it established a new world speed record over a 1000km course while carrying a 1000kg payload of 664km/h (413mph). For this record attempt the I-16 was in operation for 45 minutes. The maximum speed of the XA-26F was 700km/h (435mph).

Prior to the XA-26F, Douglas had designed and built two prototypes of its XB-42 Mixmaster bomber to an Air Technical Service Command contract, these having flown on 6 May and 1 August 1944. Apart from cockpit canopy arrangements for the pilot and copilot, the two were similar. Each had mid-mounted straight wings, a glazed fusel-

age nose for the bombardier, cruciform tail surfaces (the lower fin protecting the propellers), and rear-mounted Curtiss Electric co-axial contra-rotating propellers driven by two Allison V-1710-125 piston engines installed side by side within the center fuselage. Because of its low drag configura-

tion, powerful engine arrangement and large fuel tanks, the XB-42 had a possible range of more than 8050km (5000 miles) and a maximum speed in excess of 659km/h (410mph). Maximum warload was 3629kg (8000lb), carried in the weapons bay, but with such a heavy load range would have

been reduced dramatically. August 1945 brought an end to the war with Japan and an end to any hopes for production contracts. However, the XB-42 could boast a performance far greater than any other piston-engined aircraft in its class. Indeed, this 16,190kg (35,702lb) all-up weight bomber was only a quarter as heavy as the Boeing B-29 Superfortress and yet its performance could be compared favorably with the B-29's, which was then the mainstay of the USAAF's long-range heavy bomber force.

At this stage Douglas turned to jet bombers, as it was obvious that the USAAF did not intend to procure many piston-engined bombers and fighters postwar. However, the circumstances of this changeover have often been mistakenly reported, quoting the first Mixmaster when modified as an interim jet/piston-engined bomber. This was the XB-42A. In fact the Mixmaster design was first considered for turbojet power back in 1943, before an XB-42 had ever flown. An order for two jet-powered XB43s was placed in early 1944, but the practicality of such a bomber only came about with the development of the General Electric TG-180 turbojet engine, the company's first axial-flow engine which later received the military designation J35. The TG180 not only gave a thrust of 1700kg (3750lb) for take-off, but, because it had an 11-stage axial-flow compressor, it was less thirsty for fuel and had a smaller diameter than earlier centrifugal-flow engines.

The first XB-43 took to the air on 17 May 1946, at the Muroc experimental test base in

California. Because it belonged to the USAAF and carried a military serial, this aircraft became the Air Force's first jet bomber. In most respects the XB-43 looked like the first XB-42, even having the twin separate cockpit canopies for the pilot and co-pilot. The main external changes were the introduction of air intakes for the turbojets forward of the wings, the use of a conventional tail unit, and the twin exhaust nozzles below the tailplane. Maximum speed proved to be 828km/h (515mph). A second example flew thereafter, but the bomber remained a prototype. Douglas had made history with its XB-43 but had not received a contract for production examples.

Meanwhile, in December 1945 the second XB-42 had crashed, leaving one remaining prototype. It had been decided to use this Mixmaster for experiments with auxiliary turbojet engines (not as an interim bomber for the XB-43), and in due course it reappeared as the XB-42A, powered by two V-1710-133 piston engines and two 727kg (1600kg st) Westinghouse 19XB-2A turbojets mounted in pods under the wings. The 19XB-2A had a single-stage turbine and six-stage axial-flow compressor. It is best remembered as the powerplant for the US Navy's first jet fighter, the McDonnell FD-1

Phantom, when it carried the military designation 330. The re-engined Mixmaster was flown for the first time on 27 May 1947 and proved capable of adding nearly 129km/h (80mph) to its previous maximum speed, in fact not far short of the XB-43's top speed, a remarkable feat.

In 1947 the newly created USAF Strategic Air Command received its first Boeing B-50 heavy bombers and intercontinental-range Convair B-36s. These marked the end of the line for piston-engined bombers. Five radical new bombers also flew as prototypes in 1947, all but the Northrop aircraft having been designed to a 1944 specification for an all-jet bomber and photographic-reconnaissance aircraft capable of a 1600km (1000 mile) radius of action and a maximum speed of 804km/h (500mph). The favored warload included carriage of a 22,000lb bomb or many 1000lb bombs. An atomic bomb was later added as an option. In fact the requirements were not difficult to fulfil, resulting in a mixture of tactical, medium and heavy bombers. All started at design stage as straight-wing aircraft with four engines, except for the Martin contender with six. The chosen engine for the prototypes was the TG-180 or J35, which was initially produced by General

Douglas XB-42A with piston engines and Westinghouse turbojets.

Above: The second of three North
American XB-45 Tornados.

Electric and the Chevrolet and Allison Divisions of General Motors, Allison subsequently taking over development and production of the engine.

The first of these bombers to fly was the North American NA 130, remembered as the B-45 Tornado. Except for its turbojets paired in nacelles, it was a conventional design. The protruding engine nacelles allowed the complete engines to be enclosed forward of the shoulder-mounted wings for easy maintenance. The oval-section fuselage accommodated a bombardier in the glazed nose compartment, the pilot and copilot in tandem under a long canopy and approximately nine tons of bombs in an internal bomb bay. For defense against fighters approaching from the rear it had been intended to install a radar-

North American B-45A Tornado, the major production version.

operated gun system in the tail. However, as this was not ready in time, a fourth crew member was assigned the task of firing the two 0.50 in Brownings. The tail unit was conventional except for its tailplane which had pronounced dihedral, and the undercarriage was a nosewheel type.

Three XB-45 Tornado prototypes were built for evaluation, the first flying for the first time on 17 March 1947. Maximum speed was a little over 800km/h (500mph). With the prospect of installing the more powerful J47 engine into the Tornado to increase speed and warload, the aircraft was ordered into production. The J47 was a General Electric development of the J35, giving a thrust of 2359kg (5200lb) without sacrifice of weight or dimensions. However, the first examples of the B-45A initial production version were temporarily fitted with

Convair's slender XB-46.

The one and only XB-46. Funds from this programme were redirected into the XB-53 project.

J35s, but J47s subsequently became standard on all 97 aircraft built. Compared to the XB-45, the B-45A had revisions to the bombardier's compartment and undercarriage. Fourteen were subsequently modified into TB-45A high-speed tugs for the Chance Vought all-metal target glider, the operator occupying the tail-gunner's position.

Only 10 B-45Cs were completed as tactical support bombers, each with J47-GE-13 or -15 engines, large tip-tanks to supplement the 17,034 liters (4500 US gallons) of internal fuel and other changes. Maximum take-off weight increased considerably but the maximum speed now stood at 932km/h (579mph), far greater than that of the prototypes but similar to the first production version. Greater production success met the RB-45C high-altitude photographic reconnaissance derivative, 33 of which served with Tactical and Strategic Air Commands. The RB-45C also completed production of the Tornado, although other noncombat versions were created by conversion.

B-45 bombers entered service from late 1948 with the 47th Bombardment Group, based in the United States and Europe. The RB-45C served also in the Far East. Like its stablemate, the F-86 Sabre fighter, it saw action during the Korean War of the early 1950s. In retrospect the Tornado was the second most successful bomber of the original four, giving the USAF a decade of service. However, its adherence to convention in all but engines allowed it neither the production run nor length of service of the Boeing B-47, another of the 1947 prototypes and one that took best advantage of the turbojet engine. The B-45 was, however, the USAF's first four-engined jet bomber and first jet bomber in operational service.

Before the B-47 is described, mention has to be made of the Convair XB-46 and Martin XB-48. The XB-46 was the second of the 1947 bombers to fly, the one and only example flying for the first time on 2 April. This was a rather beautiful bomber with refined lines, representing the Consolidated Vultee Aircraft Corporation's (Convair) first such aircraft with turbojet engines. The latter were four J35-C-3s built by the Chevrolet Division of General Motors, grouped in pairs in nacelles which also housed the main units of the retractable undercarriage. The thin high aspect radio wings were mounted high on the long and slender oval-section cigar-shaped fuselage. Although the XB-46 carried no armament or radar for the manufacturer's and USAF flight trials, a notable feature of the

aircraft was its long bomb bay, fitted with fast-opening doors. The specified crew of three comprised a pilot and copilot seated in tandem under a fully-transparent fighter-type bubble canopy and a bombardier in a forward compartment fitted with a one-piece nose transparency. Normal maximum take-off weight of the XB-46 was 41,277kg (91,000lb), which included 16 1000lb bombs, although a 22,000lb bomb could be carried. Maximum speed, however, was disappointing, despite the aircraft achieving an aver-

age of 858km/h (533mph) on part of its delivery flight to the USAF's Wright Field, Ohio. Range was 4619km (2870 miles) with a warload of 3628kg (8000lb), and service ceiling was approximately 13,000m (43,000ft). The XB-46 was not selected for service with the

USAF and neither was a projected photographic reconnaissance variant reportedly designated XF-21 (the USAF using 'F' designations for reconnaissance aircraft up to 1947).

Of course, the Convair company had

Convair B-36 with four auxiliary turbojet engines under the outer sections of the wings.

achieved great success with its B-36 pusher-engined strategic bomber, which not only was the largest US military aircraft in production at the period, but was the USAF's largest-ever bomber and the first strategic bomber with true intercontinental range. First flown as a prototype in August 1946, several versions were built, the B-36D third production model of 1942 introducing four J47 turbojet engines in pairs on pylons under the outer sections of the wings to supplement the six Pratt & Whitney R-4360 radial engines. This modification increased the bomber's over-target speed by 93km/h (58mph) to 707km/h (439mph). Maximum take-off weight also rose by nearly 13,600kg (30,000lb). The RB-36D was a reconnaissance variant of the B-36D. The RB-36E was a strategic reconnaissance modification of the B-36A with turbojets added and B-36F, H and J and RB-36F and M were later bomber and reconnaissance production aircraft respectively, all powered by radials and turbojets.

From the B-36 Convair developed the YB-60, two prototypes of which were built, the first flying on 18 April 1952. Completed to a USAF contract of March 1951, the YB-60 used a B-36 fuselage with a modified and pointed nose, a new tail unit and most importantly eight Pratt & Whitney J57 turbojets grouped in pairs under a new swept wing with a 62.97m (206ft) span (a reduction over the B-36's span of 7.3m (24ft). The J57, with a

Convair's eight turbojet-engined YB-60, pitted against the Boeing.

thrust rating of 3946kg (8700lb) in early form, was eventually to power many of the military and civil aircraft produced in the US, but at this time another important prototype it powered was the Boeing B-52. It was to compete against the B-52 that the YB-60 had been requested by the USAF.

Returning to the 1947 bombers, the third to fly after the XB-45 and XB-46 was the XB-48. Produced by the Glenn L Martin Company, it was the first US bomber with six turbojet engines and flew for the first time in June. The first was delivered to the USAF for testing on 25 July. In many ways it was similar to the XB-45, having thin shoulder-mounted wings, a conventional tail unit with considerable tailplane dihedral, a tandem cockpit for the pilot and co-pilot and a nose compartment for the bombardier, and remotely controlled tail guns. The fuselage was comparatively short but deep, with the bomb bay positioned between the two pairs of mainwheels that retracted into the fuselage. Three Allison-built J35-A-5 turbojet engines were grouped in an angular nacelle under each wing. The outer sides of the nacelles housed the retractable stabilizing wheels of the undercarriage. Two XB-48 prototypes were built and their maximum speed was around 885km/h (550mph). The type failed to win production orders.

The second Boeing XB-47 stands alongside a piston-engined Boeing B-50.

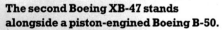

Interestingly, Martin was a little more successful applying turbojets to Navy aircraft, actually delivering 19 P4M Mercator long-range patrol aircraft to the US Navy from 1950. Each was powered by two Pratt & Whitney R-4360-4 radial engines and two Allison J33 centrifugal-flow turbojets, the latter housed in the rear of the same nacelles used by the radials and fed with air via intakes below the forward cowlings. Carrying a crew of ten, guns for defense and a heavy warload of bombs or mines, it could cruise at nearly 466km/h (290mph) on the radials alone and dash at a speed well over 160km/h (100mph) greater with all engines running.

A later attempt by Martin to produce a four turbojet-engined patrol flying-boat in the mid-1950s, brought about the P6M Sea-Master for the US Navy, which had a maximum speed of 966km/h (600mph). Just six pre-production and three production Sea-Masters followed the prototypes, but none became operational. Ironically, the only true bomber turbojet-powered produced by Martin to reach operational status was its B-57, a license-built version of the British Canberra.

By far the most important of all the 1947 bombers was the Boeing B-47 Stratojet. Although this first flew as a prototype on 17 December and therefore after the Northrop

Martin's six-jet XB-48

YB-49, it was the last of the four bombers built to the original 1944 specification and so has to be mentioned first. The Stratojet also had the honor of becoming the USAF's first six-engined production jet bomber, the jet bomber built in greatest quantity in the western world and the first large bomber in the world with sweptback wings and tail surfaces.

The aircraft which is remembered as the Boeing Model 450 or B-47 Stratojet was very different from that proposed originally to the USAAF to fulfill the 1944 specification. Indeed, after the first proposal which covered a straight-winged bomber with four turbojet engines in paired nacelles as the Model 424, Boeing considered other con-

figurations with straight and swept wings and with the engines in the fuselage. The idea of using swept wings at all had been one consequence of a visit to Germany by Boeing engineers after the war in Europe had ended. However, any thoughts of using the new jet against Japan were ended in August 1945. It was soon after this date that the latest Boeing design proposal featured sweptback wings for the first time, but still the design was unsatisfactory and so a new configuration was proposed as the Model 450.

The Model 450 was a shoulder-wing medium bomber, the thin wings having a 35 degree angle of sweepback. Six J35 turbojets were installed, two in pods near the wingtips and four in pairs on forward-swept pylons between the outer engines and the

The first Boeing B-47A Stratojet. Note the glazed nose, a feature of the B-47A and B.

fuselage. Auxiliary power for take off was provided by a total of 18 Aerojet solid-fuel JATO rocket motors (nine each side) installed within the fuselage aft of the wings. These provided a thrust of 8165kg (18,000lb) and were used to shorten take-off runs, allowing the bomber to use existing runways. Subsequently a ribbon-type braking parachute was developed for the bomber to reduce the landing run. As adopted by North American, Convair and Martin for their bombers, the crew comprised a pilot and copilot in tandem under a bubble-type canopy and a bombardier in the nose, and provision was made for tail armament for defense against fighters approaching from the rear. The latter was to comprise the usual twin 0.50in guns, either radar-

controlled or remotely-controlled by the copilot. The undercarriage was not unlike that fitted to the Martin XB-48, with two twin-wheel units forming the main gear and retracting into the underside of the pods.

Two XB-47 prototypes were built, the first with J35 engines taking to the air initially on 17 December 1947, having been rolled-out five days previously. The second prototype with J47 engines flew for the first time on 21 July 1948. On 7 October 1949 the first flew with J47s, the greater thrust of these engines proving ideal for the bomber. Meanwhile, on 8 February that year a pro-totype had crossed the United States non-stop in 3 hours 46 minutes, averaging 976km/h (607mph).

With the rather unusual-looking B-36 in-tercontinental bomber going into USAF ser-vice, it would not be surprising if the 10 production B47As ordered from Boeing for operational evaluation were too futuristic for some. These were followed by 87 B-47Bs. The first of the B-47As flew on 25 June 1950. Compared to the XB-47s, the B-47A had J47-GE-11 engines and JATO rockets with a combined thrust of 9070kg (20,000lb). The maximum take off weight of 73,709kg (162,500lb) remained the same.

World events now took control over the B-47, allowing an immediate injection of finance to rush Stratojets into USAF service. On the very day the first B-47A flew, forces from North Korea moved south and the Korean War began. As mentioned previously, the first B-47As had already been ordered, changes including provision for two large underwing drop tanks and flight refueling using Boeing's 'flying boom' pressure sys-

Boeing RB-47E, one of the B-47Es produced for day and night long-range photographic reconnaissance.

tem from new KC-97A tanker aircraft. All-up weight was 83,915-90,718kg (185,000-200,000lb). The first B-47B flew on 26 April 1951 and the first 'Bs' entered service with the 306th Bomb Wing within a few months. The Korean War brought new orders for the B-47B, these covering a variant with 2630kg (5800lb st) J47-GE-23 turbojets in place of the earlier GE-11s with thrust ratings of only 2360kg (5200lb). Total production of the B-47B amounted to 399 aircraft, including some built by Douglas and Lockheed. The two outside manufacturers also produced examples of later B-47s, returning to a situation similar to that of 1943 when these companies built Boeing B-17s to speed production.

During the course of the next few years several B-47Bs were modified to fulfil other service or experimental roles. An experimental refueling tanker conversion produced the KB-47B, fitted with a British

'probe and drogue' system. Twenty-four became RB-47B high-altitude reconnaissance aircraft, each carrying eight cameras in a heated bomb-bay pack. The DB-47B was produced as the controller aircraft for the QB-47 pilotless drone, the latter being used to evaluate the vulnerability of air defenses. YDB-47B was the designation of the test aircraft for the Bell GAM-63 Rascal stand-off missile, first accepted in production form at the Pinecastle Air Force Base, Florida, in October 1957, but cancelled in the following year. More than 60 B-47Bs became TB-47B four-seat crew trainers.

There was no 'C' version of the Stratojet as such, although the designation XB-47C related to a projected four-engined variant of the B-47 originally given the military designation B-56. This bomber was proposed originally with four J35 engines in order to reduce the high cost of the B-47, Allison YJ71-A-5s later being specified. The J71 was

a very new axial-flow turbojet with a 16 stage compressor and a three-stage turbine and could be operated in all weather conditions. It had a thrust of more then 4535kg (10,000lb) and eventually provided the power for the McDonnell Demon naval fighter, Martin SeaMaster and Douglas Destroyer. However, this bomber and its photographic reconnaissance derivative were cancelled before a prototype could be flown.

XB-47D referred to two B-47s modified to flight-test the Wright YT-49 turboshaft engines, each 10,380eshp engine driving Curtiss Turboelectric propellers with ducted spinners. The first XB-47D flew for the first time on 26 August 1955. Then came the all important 'E' model, the main production variant of the Stratojet. No fewer than 1590 were built, including the final 240 produced as RB-47E day and night photographic reconnaissance aircraft (the first RB-47E flew on 3 July 1953). The B-47E was powered by

Above: One of four YDB-47Es used for the Bell GAM-63 Rascal stand-off missile development program.

six 3265kg (7200lb)st J47-GE-25 engines with water injection to increase power by 17 percent, carried flight refueling equipment and a new and more-powerful 33-rocket JATO pack that could be dropped after take-off, had a redesigned cockpit and substituted two 20mm cannon for the earlier guns. Such was the success of this refined and strengthened version – which had an all-up weight of 93,757kg (206,700lb), maximum speed of 975km/h (606mph) and range of 6438km (4000 miles) – that most B-47Bs were modified to this standard and redesignated B-47B-IIs. Eventually, a small number of B-47Es became photographic and weather reconnaissance aircraft, test aircraft for the Rascal program, special electronic communications types, and reconnaissance aircraft for searching out radar stations. The first B-47E flew on 30 January 1953.

In early 1957 production of the B-47 finally ended for Strategic Air Command. At about this time the B-47s in operational use were modified structurally to allow between six and ten more years of service. LABS (low altitude bombing system) or 'toss' bombing thereafter became an operational technique for delivering tactical nuclear weapons at low level, with the pilot pulling the aircraft up sharply before weapon release and then rolling away on a half loop. However, this maneuver was dropped from the B-47's tactical repertoire

subsequently, although the bomber continued its combat role. The very last B-47s finally left the USAF in 1969, having served for the last three years in the passive role of weather reconnaissance.

Worthy of mention was Boeing's 1948 project for a long-range bomber derivative of the B-47. This bomber was to have had high-mounted wings with 21 degree sweepback, a span of 41m (135ft), length overall of 36.25m (118ft 11in), and a designed maximum take-off weight of 61,235kg (135,000lb). Maximum speed at 9150m (30,000ft) was estimated to be 789km/h (490mph), service ceiling 12,830m (42,100ft) and range 8585km (5333 miles). Bombload was to be between 4535-11,340kg (10,000-25,000lb). Selected powerplant was four Allison T40-A-2 turboprops driving Aeroproducts co-axial contra-rotating propellers, each with a rating of 5525shp. Although the XB-55 remained on the drawing board, the T40 powered several aircraft, including the Douglas A2D Skyshark and North American A2J attack aircraft, and the Convair P5Y flying-boat, none of which entered service. The engine had greater success with the later Tradewind flying-boat. Interestingly, Boeing's belief that very long range coupled with high performance could only be achieved by a bomber fitted with turboprop engines manifested itself again when the B-52 was conceived with turboprops. Similar thinking in the Soviet Union produced the Tupolev Tu-95 which, unlike the B-52, retained turboprops.

The final 1947 bomber built for the USAF had no direct connection with the XB-45,

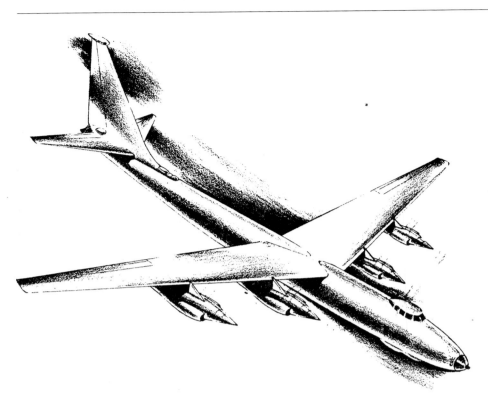

Artist's impression of the Boeing Model 474/XB-55.

XB-46, XB-47 and XB-48, not having been developed to fulfill the 1944 specification. In many ways the Northrop YB-49 was the most adventurous and, hard as it is to believe, very nearly became a service bomber. Indeed, it was probably the very radical configuration of the bomber as much as any other admitted reason that prevented its selection for large-scale use. The facts bear this out. In early 1949 one YB-49 flew a distance of 3634km (2258 miles) between Muroc Air Force Base, California, and Washington DC, averaging a speed during the flight of 822km/h (511mph). On another occasion, a YB-49 demonstrated a service ceiling in excess of 12,190m (40,000ft) during a flight lasting 9.5 hours. Such performance on the power of eight J35-A-19 turbojets was remarkable.

The YB-49 origins go back beyond the United States' entry in World War II. In 1940 Northrop flew its experimental N-1M flying-wing aircraft, a diminutive single-seater built to flight test the configuration for a projected transport aircraft. Flying-wing research was not unique to the United States, much work having been carried out in Germany, Britain and elsewhere. However, the work undertaken by Northrop was among the most successful and advanced and led the company to suggest to the USAAF a bomber based on the flying-wing concept. This was some three months before the

attack on Pearl Harbor. With the outbreak of the Pacific War, the go-ahead was given for development. As a first step towards a production bomber, Northrop developed one-third scale flying models of the bomber to test the design and give pilots flying experience, these receiving the designation N-9M. Each was powered by two piston engines mounted as pushers.

The Northrop bomber was assigned the military designation XB-35. Interestingly the date of order, November 1941, was the same as that for the successful B-36. Both the XB-35 and XB-36 made use of Pratt & Whitney R-4360 Wasp Major piston engines driving pusher propellers, but the former required only four. When the XB-35 was completed in 1946 it presented to the world a most unusual sight. Here was a 52.43m (172ft) wing, constructed in the open in one piece from aluminum alloy. The chord at the centerline was an amazing 11.43m (37ft 6in), and the wing area was no less than 371.6sq m (4000sq ft). However, even these giant proportions were nothing when compared to those of the B-36, which appeared soon after. The crew comprised a pilot seated in the forward offset cockpit under a bubble canopy, a copilot, engineer, navigator, bombardier and gunner. Defensive armament was located in two four-gun turrets and four two-gun turrets spread above

The first of Northrop's amazing YB-49 jet-powered flying-wing bombers. Note the eight engines in groups of four.

YB-49 in graceful flight.

and below the wing, controlled by the gunner from his cockpit in the rearward-protruding tail nacelle.

The XB-35 flew for the first time on 25 June 1946 and this was followed by an order for 13 YB-35 development and service test aircraft. However, the advantages of turbojet power for the flying-wing bombers were quickly realized and two YB-35s became YB-49 eight-jet prototypes. Of the remaining YB-35s, most are thought to have been considered for conversion to six-jet bombers, one to flight test Turbodyne tur-

boprop engines and four to be cannibalized. In the event a six-jet version of the YB-35 did appear, but as the experimental YRB-49A reconnaissance-bomber. Such was the success of the YB-49s, the first having made its initial flight on 21 October 1947, that a production order for an initial batch of 30 B-49s was placed in the following year. But, for whatever reason, the whole batch of B-49s was cancelled in early 1949.

So ended the first-generation US jet bombers. North American and Boeing were contented with production orders for their B-45 Tornado and B-47 Stratojet, Convair, Douglas and Martin had to return empty

handed to the drawing board (although each had other military and civil aircraft underway) and Northrop gave up the flying-wing with all its promise for more conventional configurations. One point was certain, while Britain was the first nation outside Germany to develop a successful jet fighter, when it came to jet bombers no nation on earth could equal the early impetus of the United States.

This good head-on view of a YB-49 shows the full span of the flying-wing bomber.

10: WITH A LITTLE HELP

During World War II Soviet combat aircraft production was based firmly on conventionally-configured and conventionally-powered fighters and bombers. Unlike Britain, Germany, Japan and the United States, the Soviet Union had not produced a jet fighter for production, although some piston-engined fighters had been boosted by auxiliary rocket motors. When it was announced in the Soviet Union, therefore, that one of its pilots had indeed engaged the Luftwaffe over Berlin in May 1945 while piloting a jet-propelled aircraft, it had to be considered whether this referred to a boosted conventional aircraft, a captured German jet or a hurriedly prepared experimental jet using turbojet engines under development by Arkhip Mikhailovich Lyulka. Initial experiments towards a turbojet engine by Lyulka had in fact begun in the late 1930s, but these had been forced to end with the outbreak of hostilities. An improved turbojet was bench-run in 1944 as the 1300kg (2866lb st) TR-1, but the type was not in production by the end of the war.

Meanwhile, when the war against Germany was in its last throes and Soviet forces moved into Germany itself from the east, several major factories and research establishments were taken over. Immediately technicians were sent in to study the projects being worked on, to send data and equipment back to the Soviet Union for evaluation, and subsequently to organize a temporary resumption of limited work for the

Previous page: The tactical support version of the Vautour was the II-A.

Tupolev's Tu-14 bomber operated by the Soviet Navy.

benefit of the occupation forces. As well as the capture of several Junkers, Heinkel and other factories, Soviet forces took over the highly-secret research establishments at Peenemünde and Rechlin. The capture of vast amounts of technical data and working examples of several German turbojet and other engines were much prized, enabling early production in the Soviet Union of the Jumo 004B and BMW 003A for its MiG and Yak first-generation fighters. The Walter and Argus works were also captured, providing material on liquid-fueled rocket motors and ramjet engines respectively.

Soviet technicians were delighted to send home the unfinished Junkers Ju 287 prototypes. Much was expected of these. In 1946 many German scientists and technicians left Germany for the USSR, among them Junkers staff that went to Podberezhye to help with the completion of the Ju 287 with sweptback wings (project EF131). It is said that from this work were inspired a twin-turboprop bomber and other prototypes. Whatever benefit accrued from the completion of the Ju 287, it appears that few of the aircraft's innovations found their way into early Soviet bombers.

Perhaps the greatest boost to the development of Soviet jet aircraft came about in 1947, when Britain exported 25 of its well-proven Rolls-Royce Nene and 30 Derwent 5 turbojets to that nation. This export was sanctioned by the President of the Board of Trade, who set aside objections from the manufacturer and the Air Ministry. It was argued that the engines were not bound by security restrictions and thus could be exported. These engines were a great improvement over German types and allowed lengthy development of low-thrust turbojets in the Soviet Union to be bypassed. Nenes

and Derwents found their way immediately into fighter and bomber prototypes, while both types were further developed and put into mass production as RD-45s (Nenes) and RD-500s (Derwents). Soon after import, the bureau, led by V Ya Klimov, was given the job of improving upon the RD-45, producing the very important VK-1 with a thrust rating of 2700kg (5952lb) compared to the Nene's 2268kg (5000lb st) in its original form.

In 1946 it was reported that a four-engined jet bomber had been seen at Tushino, Moscow, during the Aviation Day display and flypast. Very little is known of this aircraft, which was clearly only experimental, but it was probably a reworked Petlyakov Pe-8. The 1947 May Day flypast included some 100 jet aircraft, but no jet bombers as such. Then on 3 August during the Aviation Day celebrations, new jet bomber prototypes were seen for the first time, including a four-engined bomber from Ilyushin and a smaller twin jet from Tupolev. Contemporary reports also suggest that the prototypes included a jet bomber from Sukhoi. What this could have been is not clear, although it appears most likely to have referred to either the first generation Su-9 or Su-11. The former was no more than a Soviet built Me 262 with RD-10 engines, while the Su-11 was developed from it as a ground-attack aircraft with TR-1 engines.

The honor of being the Soviet Union's first jet bomber to fly goes to the Ilyushin Il-22, it taking to the air for the first time on 24 July 1947. Constructed before the delivery of British turbojet engines, it was therefore powered by four TR-1 engines installed in forward-protruding underwing pods. Interestingly, the engines were not grouped in pairs as might have been expected because of German influence. The circular-

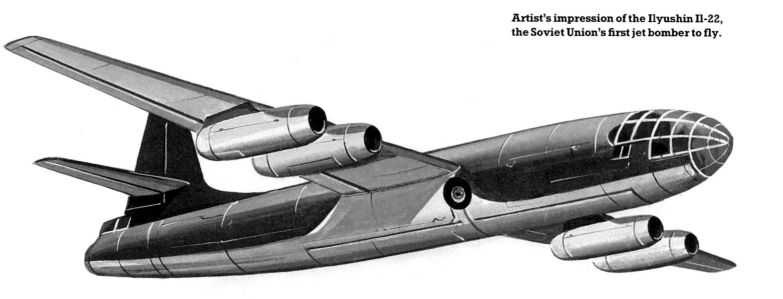

Artist's impression of the Ilyushin Il-22, the Soviet Union's first jet bomber to fly.

section fuselage was very much like that of the Tupolev Tu-4, itself a copy of the Boeing B-29 Superfortress. The most obvious difference was the newly-designed glazing, with a larger-area, unbroken panelled nose section and many more side windows. Close to the leading edges of the high-mounted tapering wings were the wells for the retracted units of the nosewheel-type undercarriage. The tail unit was conventional. Armament comprised up to 3000kg (6614lb) of bombs carried in the fuselage bay and a choice of two 23mm NS-23 cannon or 12.7mm Beresin machine-guns in both tail and dorsal turrets.

Only one Il-22 was built and this was not a success. However, in the sidelines was Ilyushin's Il-28. The other jet bomber to fly during the Aviation Day display of 1947, the Tupolev Tu-12, faired little better but was probably intended from the outset as an experimental design only. In fact the Tu-12, otherwise known as the Tu-77, first flew only three days after the Il-22. It seems unlikely that initial flights were made on the power of British Derwent engines, but certainly these were subsequently fitted in the very large nacelles which also housed the main units of the nosewheel-type undercarriage. The Tu-12 was obviously based on the piston-engined Tu-2, major changes being made only to the powerplant, undercarriage, and crew accommodation. Unlike the Il-22 with its crew of five, the Tu-12 had a crew of four comprising a pilot and naviga-

tor in a redesigned cockpit and two gunners to man the rear dorsal and ventral positions. The fuselage nose was both lengthened and slimmer than that of the standard Tu-2, with heavy glazing for the navigator who also acted as a bombardier.

The Soviet requirement of 1946 for a jet-powered tactical bomber suited to operational service had still to be fulfilled and for this appeared three contenders. One was from the Sukhoi team and carried the designation Su-10. It was intended to have four Soviet-designed and built TR-1A turbojet engines, probably to be carried on mountings built out from the forward wing spar and grouped in pairs with one engine on top of the other. Each upper engine was positioned well back from the lower. Interestingly, while the tailplane was unswept but tapered, the vertical tail was heavily swept. Work on the prototype continued until 1948, when the aircraft was abandoned. The reason for this is not clear but might have been influenced at least by Stalin's personal preference for the Ilyushin Il-28.

In fact it was not the Ilyushin bomber that first appeared in prototype form and there has been some confusion as to whether the Tu-14 or the Il-28 was the first jet bomber to enter service with the Soviet forces. While it is clear that the Tu-14 was the first jet bomber to be used by Soviet Naval Aviation, the Il-28 first went to the Air Force. A clue to the timing is in the state acceptance trials. Those for the Il-28 were completed in early

1949, whereas the Tu-14 trials ended later. Also, no fewer than 25 early examples of the Il-28 took part in the 1950 May Day flypast led by Lt Col A. Anpilov, all probably production aircraft.

In 1946 preliminary design of a jet bomber to compete with the Su-10 and Il-28 was initiated at the Tupolev bureau. This allowed for turbojet engines in nacelles at the extremities of the wing center-section. With the arrival of British Nene and Derwent engines in the Soviet Union, this design was radically changed to produce the follow-on Type 73. This had Nene engines in underwing nacelles and a Derwent in the tail, an air intake for the latter being incorporated into the long extension to the low-aspect-ratio, rounded fin. The wings were unswept and tapered, but the tailplane was given considerable sweepback. The mainwheels of the nosewheel-type undercarriage retracted into the nacelles. In the cockpit under a raised hood sat the pilot and radio operator in typical Shturmovik fashion, with the radio operator facing rearwards to aim and fire the remote dorsal cannon. The navigator's compartment was in the glazed nose and the rear-gunner occupied a cabin under the tailfin extension to operate the two remotely-controlled ventral cannon. In the nose of the bomber was a fixed cannon.

The type 73 took off for its first flight in October 1947 and was tested at the works for nearly eight months. Meanwhile, a second prototype joined the Tu-73, under

Ilyushin Il-28 *Beagle*, one of five operated
by the Egyptian Air Force.

the designation Tu-78. Despite some minor changes to the configuration, this aircraft was important primarily as it flew with Soviet-built RD-45 and RD-500 Nene/Derwent derivative engines. Such was the reliability and power of these, that it was considered unnecessary to retain the tail-mounted Derwent for production bombers. It was, indeed, the continual reappraisal of the design that lost Tupolev the lead over Ilyushin for the honor of producing the Soviet Union's first production jet bomber. The tail-mounted engine was duly removed on a new prototype, allowing for a conventionally-operated defensive system of twin Nudelman-Richter NR-23 cannon in a lengthened tail, while the dorsal cannon were removed and the nose armament doubled. The rear-gunner's cabin became the accommodation for the bombardier. Externally the most recognizable change was to the vertical tail, which became more angular. As the Tu-81, the aircraft was accepted for production and became a naval attack bomber for shore-based duties, carrying the new designation Tu-14.

Several versions of the TU-14 were produced, the most important being the Tu-14T, carrying up to 3000kg (6614lb) of bombs or two torpedoes. Most Tu-14s, which received the NATO reporting name *Bosun,* were powered by two VK-1 engines. Maximum speed at height was 845km/h (525mph) and maximum range with a light warload was a little over 3000km (1865 miles). It is not known how many Tu-14s were built for the Soviet Navy, but it is likely to have been a comparatively small number. These served throughout most of the 1950s and into the next decade. The Tu-14 also failed to win the international acceptance that greeted the Il-28.

In March 1952 Andrei Tupolev and 13 members of his design bureau received a Stalin Prize of 150,000 roubles, undoubtedly for their major contributions to the development of jet bombers. A similar prize was awarded to Sergei Ilyushin and 10 of his team, prompted by the success of the Il-28.

It is true to say that the Ilyushin Il-28, known to NATO as *Beagle* in its combat form, was one of the most successful jet bombers ever built. It was undoubtedly built in the greatest numbers, had the longest production run and was the most widely operated. In the early 1980s it was still in production in China as the Harbin B-5, carrying the Chinese name Sinshi-wu Houng-chai Chi. It is believed that the Air Force of the People's Liberation Army has 300-450 Il-28 bombers in operational use,

some assigned the task of delivering nuclear weapons, while the People's Navy is thought to have 100-150. How many of these are Chinese-produced and how many are surviving aircraft from the 500 or thereabouts delivered to China from the Soviet Union prior to the political breakup is not clear. At least 19 other countries outside the USSR received Soviet or Czech-built Il-28s at one time or another. These have included Afghanistan, which still had some 20 in 1981; Algeria, with about 24; Bulgaria, no longer used; Cuba, no longer used; Czechoslovakia, which put the Il-28 into production as the B-228 but no longer uses them; Egypt, a small number remaining; Democratic Republic of Germany, no longer used; Finland, two still in use as target tugs; Hungary, still operational but the number unknown; Indonesia, no longer used; North Korea, about 60 bombers plus trainers in use; Iraq, some 10 trainers in use; Nigeria; Poland, a few

Yakovlev Yak-28.

remaining for reconnaissance and electronic countermeasures roles; Romania, a few remaining for reconnaissance role; Somalia, a small number of bombers; Syria, about 10 for attack; Vietnam, a few bombers; North Yemen, a handful of bombers; and South Yemen with some 12 bombers. Chinese B-5s have also been exported, Albania receiving 10. The Soviet forces no longer operate Il-28s.

As mentioned earlier, the Il-28 was designed to a 1946 requirement for a light tactical bomber and was regarded very favorably by officials and Stalin alike. Indeed, in 1947 Stalin ordered high priority for its development and subsequently ordered that it should take part in the May 1950 flypast. Three prototypes were built, the first taking to the air initially on 8 August 1948. On the power of two RD-45 turbojets carried in underwing pods common to the Tu-12 and Tu-14, it demonstrated a maximum speed of 833km/h (567mph). However, this was reduced by nearly 80km/h (50mph) when operational equipment and armament were added.

Early series-built Il-28s had RD-45FA turbojets rated at 2740kg (6041lb)st. Subsequently the VK-1 and later versions of this engine were fitted, including the 2700kg (5952lb)st VK-1A. The Il-28 is a three-seat bomber, its shoulder-mounted wings having straight leading edges and tapered trailing edges. Construction is mostly of D16-T duralumin. The circular-section semimonocoque fuselage has a glazed nose with an optically-flat panel for bomb aiming. This task is undertaken by the navigator, who is seated on an ejection seat in a cabin below and forward of the pilot's cockpit. It is the pilot who fires the twin NR-23 cannon that are carried in a fixed position in the lower fuselage. The radio operator also has control of the two NR-23 tail-guns, each with 225 rounds of ammunition, which are carried on a Il-K6 mounting.

The radio operator has no ejection seat, having to use the entry hatch under the rear

fuselage for an emergency escape. Maximum warload carried in the internal weapons bay is 3000kg (6614lb), but like the Tu-14 the usual load was designed to be just 1000kg (2206lb) or perhaps four 500kg or eight 250kg bombs. Unlike the Tu-14, both the vertical and horizontal tail surfaces are swept, at 45 degrees and 33 degrees respectively, but the undercarriage was designed to be similar, with the main units retracting into the engine nacelles. At a normal take-off weight of 18,400kg (40,565lb), the Il-28 with VK-1A turbojets has a maximum speed of 902km/h (560mph) at 4500m (14,760ft). Range is up to 2400km (1490 miles) when flown at low speed and high altitude at the maximum take-off weight of 21,200kg (46,738lb).

Apart from the Chinese and Czech-built versions of the Il-28, the basic versions built have been the standard Il-28, which first entered service Soviet air force units in about 1950; the Il-28R reconnaissance variant, with tip-tanks as standard to increase range and endurance and carrying three, four or five cameras and flares or photoflash bombs in the bomb bay; and the Il-28T naval version carrying one or two torpedoes, depth charges or mines. The Il-28U is a training version with the bomb-aiming glazed panels and cannon removed and a second heavily-glazed but lower cockpit with dual controls installed in the forward fuselage. Also deleted is the PSB-N ground-mapping and blind-bombing radar housed in the underfuselage blister just aft of the nosewheel doors. ECM (electronic countermeasures) and other specialized variants of the Il-28 were completed by modification of standard types. Worthy of mention also is the Il-20, a specially-prepared civil version of the Il-28, used by Aeroflot briefly from 1956 to carry various cargoes associated with newspaper production between major cities.

The first swept-wing bomber to originate in the Soviet Union was the Tu-82, an experimental aircraft both smaller and lighter than the Tu-14 but considerably faster. It appeared in 1949 but was not selected for production. Ilyushin's first bomber with swept wings was the experimental Il-30, a very high-speed aircraft from which was evolved the Il-54. Capable of a speed of more than Mach 0.9, the Il-54 began testing in 1954, but this too remained experimental. However, so sure were officials in the West that the Il-54 was destined for operational service, that it was assigned the NATO reporting name *Blowlamp*.

While the West was awaiting the first

signs of *Blowlamp* in operational service, inside the Soviet Union plans were taking a different course. There was little doubt that the Il-54 was a formidable light tactical bomber, possessing a maximum speed more than 240km/h (150mph) higher than that of the standard Il-28 in service, although range was a matter for concern. Power was provided by two 6500kg (14,330lb)st Lyulka AL-7 turbojets, the first such engine having been bench run only in 1952 and the first production examples given flight clearance in 1954. In fact the Il-54 was the AL-7's first application, although soon afterwards it was installed in early examples of the Sukhoi Su-7, which in production form was the aircraft destined to replace most Il-28s. If proof was needed by 1961 that *Blowlamp* had not achieved operational status, it came with its absence from the Aviation Day flypast and the inclusion of new prototypes described as supersonic multi-purpose aircraft. These were prototypes of the Yak-28, which had flown for the first time the previous year.

Known to NATO as *Brewer*, the Yak-28 went into Soviet air force service from 1963, by which time more than a decade had passed since the first of the projected Il-28 replacements had flown. This time lapse was due more to the excellence of the Il-28 and the development of a single-engined ground-attack fighter (the Su-7) that could perform many of the Il-28's tasks, than to any inability to produce a multi-engined replacement of the necessary caliber. Indeed, it was widely accepted in the mid-1950s that *Beagle* was perhaps the most formidable tactical bomber in the world.

Brewer was produced in three attack versions, each accommodating the pilot in a fighter-type cockpit under a blister canopy and the navigator/bomb-aimer in the glazed nose. Power was provided by two 5950kg (13,117lb)st Tumansky R-11 turbojets with afterburning, a widely used engine that had entered production in 1956. These were installed in very long underwing nacelles, the wings themselves being swept back at 45 degrees. The semi-monocoque fuselage and swept tail surfaces were designed to be conventional, but the undercarriage was not, having tandem twin-wheel main units under the fuselage and small balance wheels near the wingtips. Interestingly, this type of undercarriage arrangement had previously been seen on. *Blowlamp*.

The first production version was known to NATO as *Brewer-A* and was the most basic. It carried one fixed 30mm NR-30 cannon in the forward fuselage, light weapons on underwing pylons and bombs (usually two 500kg) or nuclear weapons in the bomb bay positioned between the main undercarriage units. A pylon under each wing outboard of the engine usually carried a pointed slipper-type auxiliary fuel tank to increase range.

The next version was *Brewer-B,* a generally similar aircraft that probably became operational very soon after *Brewer-A.* The main refinement was the addition of a ventral blister radome under the fuselage forward of the wings, which housed the navigation and blind-bombing radar. This was followed by the final attack version as *Brewer-C.* This was easily identifiable by its slightly longer fuselage, lengthened engine nacelles that extended forward to a point level with the radome and long wingtip probes. Cannon armament was increased to two in the forward fuselage.

By the early 1980s most *Brewer* attack aircraft had been withdrawn from front-line duties to serve in support capacities, their light warload, transonic maximum speed and probable maximum range of no more than 1850km (1150 miles) making them unsuited to service with the modern Soviet air force. However, some 200 *Brewer-D* reconnaissance aircraft with cameras in the bomb-bay and 40 *Brewer-E* electronic countermeasures aircraft are deployed. *Brewer-E* is of particular interest as it was the first Soviet aircraft deployed as an ECM escort, having entered service in 1970. This variant also has provision for carrying rocket pods outboard of the auxiliary slipper tanks. The Yak-28P two-seat, all-weather fighter was also derived from *Brewer* attack aircraft and is known to NATO under the reporting name *Firebar.* Up to 300 serve today in air defense units, having been operational for close-on two decades. The designation Yak-28U applies to a tandem cockpit trainer for *Firebar* pilots, known to NATO as *Maestro.*

Another country that benefited from the British Rolls-Royce Nene engine was France, whose own engine manufacturers were not able to produce turbojets of this caliber for some years after the war. This is not to say that French companies had been slow to grasp the importance of the turbojet as a powerplant for aircraft. Far from it. The Société Rateau had started experimenting in this field as early as 1939, but the German occupation of France ended any real hope of major advances. However, small groups of the company's engineers worked continuously during this period, allowing clandestine achievements to be co-ordinated postwar and the SRA-1 axial-flow turbojet

The French Sud-Ouest SO 4000 high-performance bomber carrying a civil registration.

engine to be built. By early 1947 the engine had completed acceptance trials but was clearly not in the same class as turbojets being produced abroad. Work thereafter began on the SRA-101 10-stage axial-flow engine, with a static thrust of 4000kg (8820lb), in collaboration with SNECMA.

Another company that continued work on gas turbine engines while under German authority was SOCEMA, who in fact managed fairly open development of a turboshaft engine by adopting the pretense of working on an engine for a train. This deception was aided by the choice of designation for the engine, TGA 1 assuming to stand for Turbo-Groupe d'Autorail and its development being under contract from the French railway authority.

In the long term it was the work started

by Aeroplanes G Voisin, Groupe Technique, which had the major effect on later French jet aircraft design. This group took over the design department of Atelier Technique Aéronautique Reichenbach after the war, the company itself having previously been engaged in the manufacture of BMW engines at its Lake Constance plant. Work was swift and soon the ATAR 101 seven-stage, axial-flow turbojet had been developed in prototype form, the actual construction of the engine being the responsibility of SNECMA. Testing began on 11 May 1948 at Paris and early flight trials were conducted using a Martin B-26 Marauder.

As mentioned previously, Hispano-Suiza began the production of turbojet engines following the receipt of licenses from Rolls-Royce covering the Nene and Tay. The license for the Nene was granted in 1946, as a result of which several prototype jet aircraft were rapidly completed. However, it should not be forgotten that early experi-

ments in France included those with jet air- craft powered by German engines, the Arsenal VG 70 single-seat research aircraft being an example. Using French-built Nenes, the Aérocentre NC 1071 became the first French multi-jet aircraft to fly, taking off for the first time on 12 October 1948. De- signed as a carrier-borne trainer for the French Navy, it had been projected also for torpedo and dive-bomber roles.

The NC 1071 was an interesting design, with its crew of two or three occupying a central nacelle and two very large outer nacelles housing the engines and also sup- porting the tail unit with twin fin and rudder and a linking horizontal surface. The main- wheels of the nosewheel undercarriage re- tracted into the engine nacelles and the offset nosewheel into the central nacelle. The wings were unswept and tapered. Max- imum take-off weight was reported to be 11,450kg (25,240lb) and maximum speed 792km/h (492mph). Although an important

design in respect of its powerplant, it was one of the casualties of the company's voluntary liquidation in 1949. A twin-jet bomber designated NC 270, was designed to achieve a speed of Mach 0.88 on the power of Nenes and had swept wings and tail surfaces. It too was a casualty of the liquidation when the prototype was 85 per- cent complete.

Interestingly, prior to the start of con- struction of the NC 270 jet bomber pro- totype, Aérocentre had built and flown two scale flying models as NC 271s. The first was flown as a glider to test the general configuration, but the second was powered by a Walter rocket motor housed in the fuselage. The glider was first released from an SE 161 Languedoc 'motherplane' on 28 January 1949, only a few months before the company ended trading.

A similar approach was adopted by SNCASO, a company best remembered simply as Sud-Ouest, which projected a

twin-jet, high-performance bomber using the French-built Nene, covered under the designation SO 4000. This was a fairly sim- ple design, although it incorporated a suf- ficient number of innovations to warrant ini- tial flight trials with half-scale models. The SO 4000 was designed to accommodate a crew of two under a fighter-type canopy high in the nose of the long and deep cigar- shaped fuselage. Forward of the swept back wings were air intakes for the Nene engines that were positioned side-by-side in the rear fuselage. The tail unit was con- ventional except for the low position and sweep of the tailplane, but the undercar- riage was another matter entirely. This used a very long nosewheel and four individual mainwheels in tandem pairs that retracted into the wing roots.

The first half-scale model was the SO M1 glider. This was followed by the M2, ex- pected to research high-speed flight and for this purpose carried a Rolls-Royce Derwent in the rear fuselage. Take-off was achieved on 13 April 1949 and in the following year M2 became the first French aircraft to exceed a speed of 1000km/h in level flight. It had thick-skinned, laminar-flow wings, swept at 31 degrees and with wide trailing-edge flaps. Small ailerons connected with spoilers for lateral control and leading-edge slots were incorporated.

One of the main functions of the M2 had been to flight-test control systems at high altitude and at high subsonic speeds. When this was achieved the SO 4000 prototype was completed and flown for the first time on 15 March 1951. A cruising speed of 830km/h (516mph) was, estimated for the bomber, but it was soon after abandoned.

Even at this early stage it had become quite clear that the SO 4000 was not an advanced design, despite its swept wings and tailplane. A glance at aircraft appearing in Britain, the US and the Soviet Union was testament to this. However, in the sidelines was a new aircraft from Sud-Ouest, although it is better remembered as a Sud-Aviation type following the amalgamation of Sud-Ouest and Sud-Est (SNCASO and SNCASE) in March 1957. This was the SO 4050 Vautour, a high-performance 'Jack of all

trades.' Said to have derived from the SO 4000, there is little evidence of this from a cursory glance at the two aircraft, although no doubt much of the research data gained from the SO M2/SO 4000 program was useful to the SO 4050 project.

The SO 4050 was among the first aircraft to have Atar 101 engines installed, marking the coming-of-age of the French-developed turbojet. Indeed the Atar in various models has powered all operational French jet fighters and bombers since the Vautour, although the very latest combat aircraft of French origin have turned to turbofans. The Vautour was conceived to fulfill three main roles, namely tactical support (fighter-bomber), bomber and all-weather fighter. The first of three prototypes took to the air for the first time on 16 October 1952 on the power of two Atar 101Bs. This aircraft was subsequently re-engined with Atar 101Cs. The second prototype did not fly until 16 December 1953, using Atar 101Ds followed nearly a year later by the third prototype with Armstrong Siddeley Sapphire 6 engines. These prototypes were the fighter, tactical support and bomber variants respectively. Also in 1953 the French government ordered six preproduction aircraft.

The first was the two-seat bomber fitted with afterburning Atar engines, which became the property of the air force on 25 March 1955. The next two preproduction Vautours were single-seat tactical support types, followed by three two-seat fighters, the last powered by Rolls-Royce Avon turbojet engines was flown in October 1955.

When the production Vautour was ordered for the French air force, the initial request for 140 was expected to be only the first, a total strength of 360 then being envisaged. However, 140 remained the total number built, comprising 30 Vautour II-A tactical support aircraft, 40 II-B bombers and 70 II-N fighters. The first to enter service was the II-A in 1956. By early 1959 all of this version, 25 of the II-Bs and half the II-Ns had been delivered. In the following year six II-Bs were acquired from France by Israel, as well as all but five of the II-As. All production Vautours were powered by Atar 101E-3 engines, each rated at 3500kg (7716lb)st.

The Vautour represented several 'firsts,' apart from those connected with its configuration. These included the SO 4050-01 becoming the first French twin-jet to break the sound barrier (while in a shallow dive), and in January 1958 one Vautour became the

first French jet to be refueled in the air. The tanker for this experiment was an English Electric Canberra.

The Vautour itself was a rather beautiful mid-wing combat aircraft, with thirty-five degrees of sweepback on its wings. Vortex generators (known also as turbulators) were positioned forward of the ailerons to increase the relative speed of the boundary layer and hold it. The turbojet engines were carried under the wings in long nacelles, which also housed the small balancer wheels of the undercarriage that retracted into the outboard sides. Main undercarriage units comprised tandem twin-wheels, retracting fore and aft of the bomb bay. A ribbon-type braking parachute was carried in the rear fuselage. An all-moving swept tailplane and swept fin and rudder comprised the tail unit, although a small rounded ventral fin was incorporated under the extreme end on the fuselage to protect the engine nacelles and nozzles on take off.

Accommodation varied according to role. The II-A had a pilot only in a pressurized cockpit sitting on an ejection seat. The

The French Vautour II-B bomber, identifiable by its glazed nose.

II-B and II-N were both two-seaters with pressurization and ejection seats, the former with a pilot under a II-A type canopy and a bomb-aimer in a nose compartment with glazed panels, who entered via a hatch forward of the pilot's canopy, and the latter with the crew in tandem under a long canopy. As with accommodation, armament varied, the II-A carrying four 30mm DEFA cannon in the nose (each with 100 rounds of ammunition), either drop tanks, four Matra rocket packs (19 rockets in each), two 450kg bombs or a total of 24 120mm rockets under the wings, and up to 10 bombs or 232 SNEB rockets in packs in the bay. The II-B's armament was similar but without the cannon, while the II-N fighter had the cannon, provision for the bomb-bay rockets and underwing stores that included the drop tanks or Matra rocket packs of previous versions, or four Matra R 511 air-to-air missiles. An automatic search and tracking fire-control radar developed by CSF was installed in the fighter. Maximum weight of the Vautour was 20,700kg (45,635lb), maximum speed 1100km/h (684mph) and range 4000km (2485 miles).

Sud-Est produced several very interesting experimental aircraft in the late 1940s

and early 1950s. One such aircraft was the Grognard, a high-speed, ground-attack jet with a peculiar 'humped back.' The fuselage shape resulted from the decision to position the air intake for the two French-built Nene turbojets aft of the pilot's cockpit, the engines themselves staggered one above the other in the deep fuselage. Other notable design features were swept back wings, a very low-mounted tailplane, and a heavily-glazed cockpit for the pilot.

The original prototype was known as the SE 2410 Grognard I. This flew for the first time on 30 April 1950. Maximum take-off weight was 14,500kg (31,967lb) and maximum speed an impressive 1037km/h (645mph) at 1500m (4920ft) altitude. Armament was expected to include cannon, rockets and bombs. In the event neither this aircraft, nor the two-seat SE 2415 Grognard II derivative that flew in the following year, achieved production status. Instead, both served as test aircraft for various weapons then under development.

Only one French bomber, the Mirage IV, has entered service since the Vautour II-B. All bombing roles, with the exception of strategic bombing, have been taken over by fighter-bombers.

11: THROUGH WAR AND PEACE -BUT NO MORE

In May 1982, an RAF Vulcan B.Mk 2 Bomber operating temporarily from Ascension Island carried out an attack at night on the Argentinian-controlled airfield at Port Stanley, Falkland Islands. Its load had been 21 1000lb bombs and its purpose to render the runway unusable by large transport aircraft. This was the first of three such attacks by Vulcans. On another two raids Vulcans carrying antiradiation missiles fired from hastily-fitted pylons attacked early warning and ground defense radars. Each raid meant a mission length of up to 16 hours and inflight refueling from Victor tankers.

Apart from their historical importance, the missions were undoubtedly at the longest range ever attempted by an air force. The eventual outcome of the conflict in the South Atlantic is now history, but these raids were carried out by aircraft of a condemned species. The last bombers of Britain's once proud V-bomber force, these aircraft had been scheduled for retirement within weeks of the conflict, half the Vulcan force having already been phased out. The fact that the remaining Vulcans could be made ready for combat and their crews prepared for such missions at this eleventh hour is remarkable enough, yet equally impressive was the speed at which new weapon systems were fitted for specialized missions and crews trained.

That an aircraft whose origins date back to 1952 should be ready for retirement cannot be in doubt, yet Britain has not developed or purchased from the United States a modern replacement. Ever since the Royal Navy began deployment of Polaris submarines, the role of the medium and strategic bomber in Britain's defenses has been run down. This process came to a head in the 1970s when forward planning clearly had no place for a manned bomber in the RAF able to strike at the strategic military and industrial targets of a potential enemy. While many argue that the threat of mutual destruction of homelands by land-based (of which Britain has none) and sea-based nuclear weapons is sufficient to prevent world war, the Falklands and other world issues have highlighted another side of military readiness. Unless planners can be sure that nuclear weapons on land or in the sea are capable of preventing all wars, and clearly they are not, it can be argued that there must be a place for manned aircraft that can not only attack invading forces

Previous page: Prototype Avro Vulcan with straight wing leading edges.

Avro Lancaster flight testing a British turbojet engine carried in the modified tail.

but can strike at the centers of military build-up, communications and production and not necessarily with weapons of mass destruction. Only the bomber can offer the instant choice of carrying conventional or nuclear weapons.

It was during World War I that Britain first discovered the importance of not only holding the front line but crippling the military production of the enemy. Only by holding up the development of new weapons and then their manufacture and deployment, could planners be sure of weakening the enemy's capacity to fight. Hastily-modified service aircraft were assigned the first strategic bombing missions, filling the

gap until purpose-designed heavy bombers became available for operation.

During World War II it was the strategic bomber that carried the war beyond occupied countries and to the homeland of the aggressor, preventing greater numbers of German conventional and jet-powered fighters and bombers from reaching units in the field, as well as holding up the development and deployment of more 'terror weapons.' The war with Japan was ended by the bomber, and bombers have been used in most postwar conflicts, from Korea to the Middle East.

It was to reinforce the wartime work of RAF Bomber Command, and to make use of early turbojet engines, that British aircraft manufacturers first decided to attempt jet bomber designs. One such project emerged from the Gloster Aircraft Com-

pany, quite understandably as this organization had previously produced the airframe for Britain's first turbojet-powered aircraft and was then busy developing the world-famous Meteor fighter. This bomber had a superficial likeness to the postwar Ilyushin Il-22, although the four W.2B engines were to be installed in partially-submerged nacelles and the wings and tail unit were clearly scaled-up from the F.9. Considering the high risk of failure surrounding such projects, it is hardly surprising that none progressed.

As mentioned previously, the British government appeared to be in no hurry to deploy a postwar jet bomber, although several interesting early designs came off the drawing boards of manufacturers such as Handley Page, Hawker and Bristol. This is not to say that the government was neg-

lecting the jet bomber as a weapon, or was attempting to smother it at birth. In some respects the opposite was true. Prior to the end of World War II Specification B.3/45 had been issued covering a light twin-jet tactical day bomber to replace the very successful de Havilland Mosquito. Provision was to be made for radar bombing equipment. A specification for a larger four-engined jet bomber to replace the Lincoln was later issued as B.14/46. Subsequently, the consensus was to accept the Rolls-Royce Avon turbojet as most suited to a bomber, this being the first axial-flow engine from Rolls-Royce and then under development as a Nene replacement. An axial-flow engine meant great fuel economy over centrifugal-flow engines.

The selection of the Avon to power the first British jet bombers meant a protracted development period, and indeed it was not

until mid-1950 that the Avon RA.3 entered production. Both the government and the manufacturers were fully aware of the delays that would be caused by using the Avon, but the possible advantages were too many to be overlooked. Anyway, nobody expected another war in the late 1940s, when disarmament was the watchword in Britain. The result was that the first British jet bombers flew as prototypes well after their American and Soviet equivalents. Had Britain been right to ignore a Nene-powered interim bomber? Equal in importance for a bomber were the twin attributes of high performance to enable it to elude jet fighters and long range. The Nene had a thrust rating of approximately 2268kg (5000lb) and a specific fuel consumption of 1.06lb/hr/lb. The Avon RA.3 gave 2948kg (6500lb) of thrust and had a specific fuel consumption of 0.88lb/hr/lb. With careful design of the airframe, an aircraft using Avons could virtually be guaranteed a winner. Happily the very nature of the turbojet engine allowed designers a field-day, because its relatively small size and lack of a propeller allowed it to be tucked away in parts of the airframe hitherto unavailable. This in itself gave rise to the possibility of achieving outstanding aerodynamic efficiency.

At an early stage in British turbojet development the Avro Lancaster had been used to flight-test the new type of power plant. Eventually the Lancastrian and Lincoln were also adopted for this purpose, testing most British turbojet and turboprop engines. The Lancastrian flight-tested the Avon, two being installed in new nacelles outboard of two piston engines. Each Avon of the development batch was known as RA.1, with either an eight or ten-stage compressor and single-stage turbine. The RA.2 refined engine had a 12-stage compressor of increased diameter and a single-stage turbine, first being flight tested on the Lancastrian on 15 August 1948.

English Electric, a company that had not designed and built an aircraft of original conception since 1926, proposed its A.1 to meet Specification B.3/45. Fortunately English Electric had experience of constructing jet aircraft if not designing them, having been entrusted with the production of the de Havilland Vampire fighter at its Preston works. Production of the Vampire had started in April 1944 and the first aircraft from Preston flew a year later.

The A.1 itself was a remarkable aircraft, flying in the face of the latest trend towards sweptback wings. Of course the company

English Electric A.1 *VN799*, first prototype of the Canberra.

One of eight Canberra PR.Mk 57 photographic reconnaissance aircraft in service with the Indian Air Force.

Canberra B.Mk 6 in RAF markings.

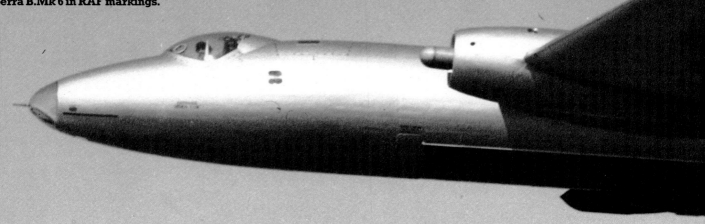

RAF Canberra T.Mk 17 electronic countermeasures trainer with a highly-modified nose.

Venezuelan-operated Canberra fitted with auxiliary tip-tanks.

was not adverse to swept wings and indeed incorporated them into its P.1 of 1954, the first British aircraft designed to fly faster than the speed of sound in level flight and progenitor of the Lightning interceptor. The A.1 was the brainchild of the company's chief designer and Engineer, W E W Petter, who had joined the company toward the end of World War II and now headed the newly-established technical and design branch. It was a mid-wing bomber with a symmetrical high-speed aerofoil section. The inner sections of the wings between the fuselage and the engine nacelles were rectangular with a dihedral angle of 2 degrees. Outboard of the engine nacelles were tapered sections, swept back on the leading-edge by 13 degrees and swept forward on the trailing-edge by 19 degrees. Dihedral on the outer sections was increased to 4 degrees. On the round-section, semi-monocoque fuselage were carried a conventional variable-incidence tailplane and a fin and rudder. Interestingly, the tail unit included some wooden structure, which was plywood covered. A nosewheel undercarriage was used. Accommodation was provided for a crew of two, the pilot under a low-profile double-layer Perspex bubble canopy seated slightly to port, and the navigator to the rear under a small roof transparency. Ejection seats and pressurization

were provided.

On 13 May 1949 the first A.1 Canberra prototype took off for its maiden flight. One of four prototypes ordered in January 1946, VN799 was piloted by Wing Commander Roland P. Beamont from the company's Warton Aerodrome. VN799 flew on the power of two RA.2s, the pre-production version of the Avon rated at 2722kg (6000lb)st. By the close of the year VN799 had accumulated nearly a hundred flying hours, a third of which were at the experimental establishment at Boscombe Down, during handling trials.

Meanwhile, the second prototype (VN813) had flown in November on the power of two Nene engines. This retrograde step was considered sensible to give the Canberra a back-up tried-and-tested engine should the newly-developed Avon fail to live up to early expectations. There need not have been any worry on that score. The two remaining prototypes were both Avon powered and flew before the end of 1949.

The four prototype Canberras were given the RAF designation B.Mk 1 and could most easily be identified from the B.Mk 2 initial production version by their lack of transparent noses. The first prototype of the B.Mk 2 flew initially on 23 April 1950 and just over a year later, in May 1951,

No 101 Squadron received the RAF's first operational B.Mk 2s at Binbrook, replacing the Lincoln. The B.Mk 2 accommodated a crew of three, comprising the pilot, the navigator/plotter to his rear and starboard, and the observer aft of the pilot. Because the B.Mk 2 relied on visual bombing the observer also acted as bomb-aimer using the sighting panels in the nose of the fuselage.

For the period preceding deployment of the V-bomber force, the Canberra was the RAF's most important bomber, gradually taking over from piston-engined bombers and forming new squadrons. Avro, Handley Page and Short Brothers joined in production to speed its entry into service. Four hundred and thirty B.Mk 2s were completed. The Canberra was also selected for service with the USAF and other air forces. For US service a modified night intruder version was developed and produced by the Glenn L Martin Company of Baltimore. To help license production, two B.Mk 2s were flown to America for study. The first of these became the first turbojet-powered aircraft to fly the Atlantic without refueling, on 21 February 1951, the flight from Aldergrove, Northern Ireland, to Gander, Newfoundland, taking just 4 hours 40 minutes. The second followed in August. Another two B.Mk 2s were delivered to Australia to help speed-up crew training in preparation

213

for the delivery of Canberra B.Mk 20s from the Government Aircraft Factories. The first B.Mk 20 actually flew on 29 May 1953, as the follow-on locally-produced production bomber to the Avro Lincoln. Power for the Australian-built Canberras was provided by locally-built Avons. It is of interest to note that the first of the two British Canberras destined for Australia flew from Lyneham to Darwin in approximately 21 hours, averaging 866km/h (538mph).

Thenceforth one version of the Canberra after another came off the production lines for the RAF and overseas customers. The PR.Mk 3 was a slightly lengthened high-altitude photographic reconnaissance version of the B.Mk 2, first flown as a prototype in early 1950. Quick to follow was the PR.Mk 7 with 3400kg (7500lb)st 109 (RA.7) engines. The T.Mk 4 was a crew trainer accommodating the pupil and instructor forward and a navigator to their rear, which entered service in 1954 and was exported. Two of the first eight Canberras built were configured at one time or another as B.Mk 5 target marker prototypes, but this version was not put into production. However, the

Martin B-57Bs in USAF service, configured as a tandem two-seat night intruders and tactical bombers.

Mk 5 was the first version to incorporate integral wing fuel tanks.

The first updated combat version was the important B.Mk 6, which used Avon 109 engines and carried more fuel. Although far fewer of these were built than of the original Mk 2, it had higher performance and is remembered as the first RAF jet bomber to be used in action, striking at anti-government forces in Malaya. Canberras also took part in the Suez campaign. The B.Mk 6 had a maximum take-off weight of 24,948kg (55,000lb), a maximum level speed of 955km/h (580mph) and a range of 6100km (3790 miles). Up to 2722kg (6000lb) of bombs could be carried in the bomb bay, this weapon load subsequently increased to include a further 2000lb of bombs, rockets or missiles under the wings. The Mk 6 also formed the basis for the B.Mk 15 and B.Mk 16 interim intruder Canberras, their armament extending to AS.30 tactical air-to-surface missiles (with 230kg high-explosive warheads) and tactical nuclear weapons.

While the last of the Canberra B.Mk 2s and Mk 6s were withdrawn from front-line duty with Bomber Command in the fall of 1961, B.Mk 15s and Mk 16s saw out the decade. B.Mk 2s and Mk 6s were thereafter converted for special duties, including radar and radio calibration and for training.

Meanwhile, in 1956 the RAF had received the first of its B(I).Mk 8 long-range night intruders. Armament eventually included four 20mm cannon in an underfuselage pack, two AS.30s or 1000lb bombs carried under the wings, and three similar bombs or tactical nuclear weapons in the bomb bay.

The PR.Mk 9 high-altitude photographic reconnaissance aircraft incorporated more changes than any previous version of the Canberra. Its wings were increased both in span and chord, power was provided by 5100kg (11,250lb)st Avon 206 engines with 15-stage compressors, and a nose station was provided for the navigator. The B(I).Mk 8's offset canopy was retained. The first flight by the prototype was achieved successfully in July 1958 and the Mk 9 entered RAF service two years later.

The PR.Mk 9 is the most important variant of the Canberra in RAF use today, although serving in small numbers. Other versions of the Canberra were produced for the RAF through production or modification but these were not combat types. Of these, the T.Mk 17 electronic countermeasures trainer, T.Mk 19 and Royal Navy T.Mk 22 target aircraft and the TT.Mk 18 target tugs were the last.

This is not the complete story of Britain's first jet bomber. Of the 1300 or so Canberras built many were produced for other air forces, which received newly-built aircraft or refurbished ex-service examples. Users included over the years Argentina, Australia, Ecuador, Ethiopia, France, India, New Zealand, Peru, South Africa, the United States, Venezuela and Zimbabwe (Rhodesia). Ironically, it was an Argentine Canberra that was one of three aircraft lost in the first air engagements of the conflict in the South Atlantic, on 1 May 1982.

Forty-eight of the Canberras built in total were the product of the Australian Government Aircraft Factories and 403 others were built in the United States under B-57 designations. Indeed, the Canberra has been the only jet-powered combat aircraft of non-US origin to have been accepted for USAF service. The distinction USAF has to be made as the US Navy/Marine Corps has accepted both the Harrier and Hawk trainer.

Reference has already been made to the two British-built Canberra B.Mk 2s that were flown to Martin in 1951. Two years later, on 20 July 1954, the first Martin license-built aircraft flew for the first time as a B-57A for the USAF. Powered by two 3266kg (7200lb st) Wright J65-W-1 13-stage axial-flow turbojet engines and incorporating some internal modifications, it had the general configuration of its British counterpart but was a two-seater. This was one of a pilot production batch of eight B-57As. Greater importance, however, was given at this stage to the similar RB-57A photographic reconnaissance version of which 67 were produced.

The first RB-57A was delivered to the USAF in March 1954. Nine months later the service received its first B-57B. This was an extensively modified derivative of the Canberra and the most important US variant. Equipped as a night intruder and tactical bomber, it introduced the tandem seating arrangement under a new long jettisonable blister canopy and with a bullet-proof windscreen forward that typified the Martin Canberra variants. Air brakes were fitted to the wings and rear fuselage. Armament comprised eight 0.50in machine-guns or four 20mm cannon, bombs in the bay attached to a revolving door (developed so that attack speed would not be lowered as with normal drag-inducing doors), and underwing pylons for 5in HVAR rockets, four bombs or napalm. The first B-57B had flown in mid-1954 and 202 were completed.

The B-57C was no more than a B-57B with dual controls, allowing the extra role of pilot training, and the B-57E was the final newly-built combat version. However, while the 'E' had provision to be used as a tactical bomber, it was also a high-speed target tug. For

A USAF Martin B-57 drops eight 750 lb bombs on a target in South Vietnam in late 1967.

One of 22 Martin EB-57B electronic
warfare training and defense evaluation
aircraft.

this role four containers housing targets could be carried externally, controls for which were in the cockpit with the cable reels and fittings being carried in the bay. These provided the opportunity for air-to-air and surface-to-air gunnery practice. All this equipment was removable for the more belligerent role.

By far the smallest number of a single version built was the 20 RB-57Ds. Developed for secret high-altitude reconnaissance duties, the RB-57D had 4990kg (11,000lb)st Pratt & Whitney J57-P-37A turbojet engines, a wing span of 32.31m (106ft) instead of the usual 19.51m (64ft), and changes in equipment.

All other versions of the B-57 were modifications and included reconnaissance and electronic warfare training and defense evaluation models (the latter first appearing as the EB-57B). The RB-57F was a high-altitude reconnaissance and radioactive particle sampling conversion by General Dynamics, with Pratt & Whitney TF33-P-11 turbofan engines (8165kg/18,000lb st) and two optional auxiliary J60-P-9 turbojets from the same manufacturer carried on two of the four wing pylons. It also had a 37.32m (122ft 5in) wing span, a new fin and rudder of increased area, new wing tanks instead of the fuselage tank, radar in a lengthened fuselage nose and electronics in the plastic wingtips. These aircraft were later redesignated WB-57F to be compatible with their use by the 58th Weather Reconnaissance Squadron at Kirtland AFB, New Mexico. The B-57G was the last conversion and comprised just 16 of the B-57Bs previously taken back into the USAF service from the Air National Guard to fight in Vietnam, and used during the final period of the conflict as night intruders. These had been modified by Westinghouse under the USAF's Tropic Moon 3 program and featured multifunction radar and other electronic equipment in the nose and chin fairings, and windows to starboard and port for infrared equipment and low light level television camera/laser rangefinder respectively. Today Pakistan still deploys B-57Bs in their original bomber role.

Britain's post-war specification for a four-engined Lincoln replacement resulted in Short Brothers' S.A.4, subsequently to be known as the Sperrin. In many aviation histories the S.A.4 is credited as having been Britain's first four-jet bomber. While it is true that the S.A.4 was built to the first such specification and construction preceded any other type, it was not the first British four-jet bomber to fly as a prototype, as this honor

Second Short S.A.4 Sperrin.

went to the Vickers Valiant.

The S.A.4 was conceived to a much more challenging specification than faced English Electric with B.3/45. B.14/46 required a bombload of up to 9070kg (20,000lb), a range of 2780km (1725 miles) while carrying half the maximum bombload, a maximum range of more than twice this with a nuclear stand-off missile in the bomb-bay, a service ceiling of 13,720m (45,000ft) and a cruising speed of 805km/h (500mph). And yet this specification was soon considered to represent a 'stop gap' bomber only.

As with the Canberra, the S.A.4 was designed to use Avon turbojets as the powerplant, these being carried in pairs, one above the other, on the unswept shoulder-mounted wings. The fuselage and tail unit were no more radical in design than the wings. Two prototypes were ordered, the first to be powered by preproduction Avon RA.2 engines and the second with initial-production RA.3s. There is no doubt that Short Brothers expected the S.A.4 to enter production for the RAF, and indeed prepared for this at prototype construction stage. This was not to be. While the two S.A.4 prototypes were being built, a proposal had been received from Vickers for a far more advanced bomber to meet Specification B.45/46. The later specification had been drawn up on 1 January 1947 to cover the development of a follow-on long-range bomber incorporating advanced design features such as swept back wings, data on which was being gleaned from captured German material and original research.

Construction of the S.A.4 prototypes had begun in 1948, but the first with RA.2 engines did not fly for the first time until 10 August 1951. The second made its maiden

flight one year and two days later. However, by then Vickers had not only completed design and construction of its bomber, but had managed a first flight, on 18 May 1951, some months prior to the Sperrin. The speed at which Vickers managed to get its bomber into the air made an interim four-jet bomber unnecessary and may be seen as the final death-blow to the Sperrin. Actually,

it is thought likely a decision not to proceed with the Sperrin had been made before either bomber flew. Nevertheless, once airborne the Sperrin proved itself an outstanding aircraft, demonstrating a maximum speed of 908km/h (564mph) and with excellent handling characteristics. In the event the two prototypes were used for nothing more belligerent than testing new engines and equipment. As for the company's activities with jet bombers, it eventually produced a total of 138 Canberras in various versions under sub-contract and as late as the 1960s was still engaged in modification programs to produce the Canberra U.Mk 10 target drones for use at Woomera, Australia, and in Malta.

Although the Vickers bomber, later to be known as the Valiant, was far more advanced than the Sperrin, it was in turn eclipsed by the two other bombers proposed to Specification B.35/46, subsequently named the Vulcan and Victor. Indeed,

Vickers Valiant V-bombers in RAF service. The center aircraft is a B.Mk 1 and on the left a B(PR)K.Mk 1.

the Valiant was the first of Britain's V-bombers to enter RAF service and the first to be retired and examples of the other two still fly today. The Vickers proposal for a bomber had not been an instant success, as prototypes were ordered under the new specification B.9/48 only after continued work on the project suggested that it could fulfill most Air Ministry requirements. There is little doubt that the Air Ministry favored the Avro and Handley Page designs. Perhaps the Valiant's greatest asset was its fairly conventional configuration, which would allow early production and so provide the RAF with a modern strategic bomber should the bomber prototypes ordered from Avro and Handley Page fail.

The Vickers Type 660 Valiant was designed as a shoulder-wing bomber with compound sweepback. Chord at the wing-root was an impressive 10.82m (35ft 6in). The circular-section semi-monocoque fuselage on production examples carried a large dielectric panel under the nose and spoilers were fitted forward of the huge bomb bay to combine with a hinged section of the lower fuselage aft to deflect the air-

flow when the bomb-bay doors were open. The tail unit was conventional, with the variable-incidence tailplane mounted midway up the slightly swept fin. Each main unit of the tricycle undercarriage comprised two wheels in tandem, retracting into the wings. Power was provided by four Rolls-Royce Avon engines installed in the trailing-edges of the inner portion of the wings, fed with air from leading-edge intakes. The crew of five was accommodated in pressurized compartments and a prone position was provided under the cabin in a teardrop fairing for the bomb-aimer. No defensive armament was considered necessary because of the aircraft's high cruising speed and altitude, but the bomb bay carried 21 1000lb bombs or a single large conventional or nuclear bomb.

Total production of the Valiant was 107 aircraft, which included the original prototypes and a single Mk 2, the final Valiant off the production line being delivered on 24 September 1957. The prototypes had been powered initially by Avon RA.3 and RA.7 engines, but the ultimate engine fitted to the Valiant was the RA.28 of 4536kg

(10,000lb) st. Production versions comprised the B.Mk 1 bomber, B(PR).Mk 1 bomber and photographic reconnaissance aircraft, B(PR)K.Mk 1 bomber/photographic reconnaissance aircraft/flight refueling tanker and receiver with a probe on the nose, and the B(K).Mk 1 bomber and refueling tanker able to carry 45,330 litres (9,972 Imperial gallons) of fuel, of which nearly half was transferable.

The B.Mk 1 first went into service with No 138 Squadron RAF, in early 1955. Several Valiant squadrons were operational by the time of the Suez crisis and took part in the fighting that followed. In March 1958 No 214 Squadron, one of those involved in the Suez campaign while operating from Malta, started development of flight refueling. It subsequently became the first squadron to be operational in the tanker role with the RAF's first purpose-built Victor tanker. Many very long-distance flights were carried out by No 214 Squadron using flight refueling. These included one on 2-3 March 1960 when a Valiant flew 13,679km (8500

miles) around the UK, remaining airborne for 18 hours and 5 minutes and carrying out two refuelings. Another in May of the same year covered 13,052km (8110 miles) in 15 hours 35 minutes, the Valiant involved flying non-stop from Marham, England, to Singapore. This aircraft was refueled over Cyprus and Karachi, Pakistan, by tankers from the same squadron.

The Valiant also dropped the first British atomic bomb and the first British hydrogen bomb. A Valiant of No 49 Squadron dropped the A-bomb on 11 October 1956 over Maralinga, Australia, and an aircraft of the same squadron released the first H-bomb on 15 May 1957 over the Christmas Island area in the Pacific. It should be noted here that this was only one year since the world's first air-transportable hydrogen bomb was dropped from a USAF bomber over Bikini Atoll on 21 May 1956.

In 1964 Valiants were ordered to change role from high-altitude to low-level bombers. This was caused by realization that the new and effective surface-to-air missiles

and interceptors in Soviet service rendered high-altitude missions extremely risky. Typical of the missiles that brought about this change was the V750VK, known to NATO as *Guideline,* which had an effective ceiling of more than 18km (11.25 miles). Part of the evidence for such a decision had come as early as 1960, when a USAF U-2 reconnaissance aircraft flying at extreme altitude was brought down by a Soviet missile. Within a year the Valiant had been retired because of metal fatigue. Maximum take-off weight with one 10,000lb bomb, but without underwing auxiliary fuel tanks, was 62,595kg (138,000lb), with an overload weight of 79,379kg (175,000lb). Maximum speed at 9145m (30,000ft) was Mach 0.84, service ceiling was 16,460m (54,000ft), and maximum range with auxiliary tanks was 7240km (4500 miles).

Britain's second V-bomber and the first jet bomber in the world to employ delta-wings, was the Avro Type 698 Vulcan. One of the three bombers proposed to Spe-

First production Vulcans under construction.

cification B.35/46, it was by far the most daring. In theory the delta wing configuration offered good handling characteristics at low and high speeds, something that the swept back wing lacked. Furthermore, a great deal of fuel could be carried in the large-area wings, leaving the fuselage clear for the bombload and equipment.

Of course, the choice of delta wings by Avro meant charting new waters and so it was decided at an early stage to flight-test one-third scale deltas on a small number of single-engined research aircraft. These were known as Avro Type 707s, the first (for low-speed handling trials) flying on 4 September 1949. Others followed for low and high-speed research, and also in two-seat configuration for pilot training. By the time of the initial Type 707's first flight the best part of two years had passed since the original proposal had been accepted by the Air Ministry.

With the information gleaned from the Type 707 research program, the final design work for the Avro Type 698 was completed. The first prototype Vulcan, fitted with four Avon RA.3 engines, flew for the first time on 30 August 1952. It was subsequently re-engined in turn with Bristol Siddeley Sapphires and in the later 1950s with Rolls-Royce Conways. The second prototype first flew on 3 September 1953, power being provided by four of the Bristol Sideley Olympus 100 turbojets specified for production Vulcans. The fuselage was lengthened slightly to eliminate the need for shortening the nosewheel during undercarriage retraction. Like the Type 707s, both

Camouflaged Valiant B(PR)K.Mk l at Marham, earmarked for display at the RAF Museum, Hendon.

prototypes featured delta wings with straight leading-edges. This planform was also used on the first few production Vulcan B.Mk 1s, the first of which took to the air on 4 February 1955. High priority was given to Vulcan production. On 5 October 1955 the second prototype had flown with modified wings and this modification became standard on all production aircraft thereafter. The new wing planform allowed for a reduced leading-edge sweep, but with compound sweep on the outer half of each wing, thereby reducing previously-encountered buffeting during high-altitude maneuvers.

The first production Vulcan B.Mk 1s had 4536kg (10,000lb)st Olympus 101 turbojets fitted in the wing trailing-edges, subsequently rerated at 4990kg (11,000lb)st. Starting with the fourteenth set of engines, Olympus 102 were substituted, rated at 5443kg (12,000lb)st, all of which were later modified

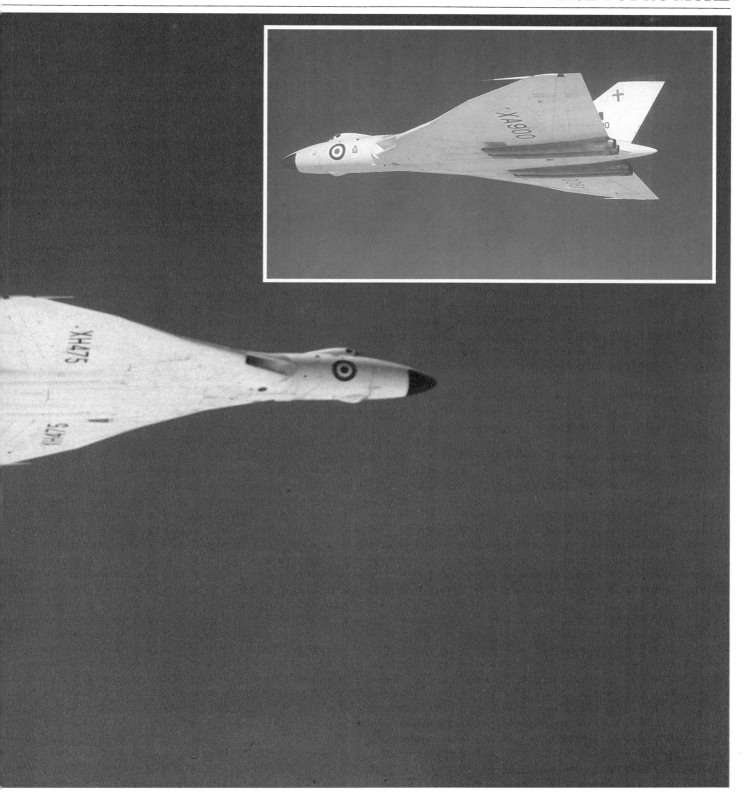

to Olympus 104 Standard, rated at 6123kg (13,500lb)st. The B.Mk 1 first became operational with No 83 Squadron in 1957 and a total of 45 aircraft was built. By 1960 the planned three squadron deployment of the Vulcan was completed. In the following year a number of B.Mk 1s were modified and redesignated B.Mk 1As, each carrying B.Mk 2-type ECM and other electronics in a bulged tail-cone. Interestingly, the second production B.Mk 1 was used for some years by the Blind Landing Experimental Unit at the Royal Aircraft Establishment, Farnborough, where development of auto-

Vulcan B.Mk 1s with the new wing shape.

Inset: Vulcan B.Mk 1 used by No 230 Operational Conversion Unit, which received Vulcans before the first operational squadron.

landing systems and other systems was conducted.

On 31 August 1957 the second prototype Vulcan took off for the first time with a larger wing as designed for the follow-on and more powerful B.Mk 2 production variant. Span was increased from 30.18m (99ft) to 33.83m (111ft), and wing area from 330.2sq m (3,554sq ft) to 368.3sq m (3964sq ft). Instead of the Mk 1's two ailerons and two elevators, each wing of the Mk 2 was given elevons. Wing aspect ratio of the Mk 1 was 2.78, that of the Mk 2 was 3.1.

The first of the production B.Mk 2s made its maiden flight on 30 August 1958 and ini-

Below: Vulcan B.Mk 2 *XH537* during Skybolt trials.

Above: Line-up of Vulcan B.Mk 2s in original anti-flash finish.

tial deliveries to No 83 Squadron began in July 1960. Production was completed at the end of 1964. The initial 7711kg (17,000lb)st Olympus 201 engines gave way during the production run to 9072kg (20,000lb)st Olympus 301s, which bestowed a maximum take-off weight of more than 81,645kg (180,000lb), a maximum cruising speed of more than 1005km/h (625mph) at 15,240m (50,000ft), a maximum cruising altitude of 16,750m (55,000ft) and an unrefueled combat radius at high altitude of 3701km (2300 miles).

Right: One of the last Vulcans built, camouflaged for low-level operations.

Blue Steel carried under a Vulcan B.Mk 2.

FIDO
INSTALLATION

Victor B.Mk 1s at a Farnborough air show.

Armament for the Mk 2 was as for the Mk 1/1A, comprising 21 1000lb bombs or free-fall nuclear weapons, but with the added provision of the Blue Steel nuclear stand-off missile, one carried semi-recessed below the fuselage of each aircraft. Blue Steel became the strategic nuclear weapon of the Vulcan from February 1963, first with No 617 Squadron. It was selected for use after extensive trials at Aberporth in Wales and the Woomera range in Australia using Valiant and Vulcan B.Mk 1 aircraft as test vehicles. The first launches of production standard missiles took place in mid-1960. For some time the US Skybolt missile had been expected to enter service as the RAF's strategic deterrent, two to be carried under the wings of a Vulcan, but this missile was cancelled in December 1962.

With the deployment of Polaris by the Royal Navy, Blue Steel was dropped and Strike Command Vulcans were given the new role of low-level attack, a task which they performed brilliantly. In 1973 a handful of Vulcans became operational with No 27 Squadron as SR.Mk 2 strategic reconnaissance aircraft, replacing Victors used in this role. The phase-out of the Vulcan B.Mk 2 planned for 1982 and the consequences to this of the Falkland Islands conflict have been mentioned previously, but on 18 June

The Handley Page Victor was designed and built with a unique crescent wing.

that year the first flight took place of a Vulcan configured for an entirely different role. This ex-B.Mk 2 had been converted in just 50 days into a flight refueling tanker, an example of what can be achieved under pressure with the right industrial backing. Within five days this first Vulcan tanker was at RAF Waddington. The modification of the bomber into a tanker entailed the installation of a redesigned hose drum unit inside the bulged tail-cone and three fuel tanks in the former bomb bay.

The third and final V-bomber was the Handley Page Victor, an aircraft that featured a unique crescent wing. This was another wing configuration that originated in wartime Germany and was basically a swept wing that became less swept, with a reduced thickness/chord ratio along its outer span. The intention was to allow an unchanging critical Mach number across the span. Initially, Handley Page had to face the problem of a lack of research into this wing configuration, as had Avro with its delta wing. There appeared no alternative but to construct one-quarter scale wings and flight test these on a modified Supermarine Type 521, resulting in a research aircraft known as the HP 88. Powered by a Nene turbojet, the HP 88 first flew on 21 June 1951. Unfortunately the aircraft was destroyed while under test before the potential of the crescent wing had been fully realized. Nevertheless, Handley Page went ahead with its full-size bomber prototype using crescent wings. Happily this turned out to be the correct decision.

Two prototype HP 80 bombers, later known as Victors, were built, the first taking to the air on 24 December 1952. The second prototype did not fly until September 1954. Initial production Victor B.Mk 1s had been ordered six months before the first prototype flew and the first B.Mk 1 made its maiden flight on 1 February 1956. The first RAF squadron to become operational with the Victor B.Mk 1 was No 10 Squadron in early 1958. By 1960 four squadrons were operational with the 50 production B.Mk 1s. Of these 24 became B.Mk 1As when fitted with ECM in the rear fuselage.

Victor B.Mk 1/1As were powered by four 4990kg (11,000lb)st Bristol Siddeley ASSa7 (or Series 200) engines, mounted within the inboard trailing-edges of the wings. In respect of their position, they were similar to the Valiants and Vulcans. Wing span was 33.53m (110ft) and wing area 223.5sq m (2406sq ft). Maximum speed was approximately Mach 0.92, which backed up the Under Secretary of State for Air's claim in 1955 that the Victor had flown close to the speed of sound at an altitude of more than 15,240m (50,000ft). In 1957 a B.Mk 1 actually exceeded Mach 1 in a shallow dive. No defensive armament was carried but the offensive load comprised 35 1000lb bombs or free-fall nuclear weapons.

In February 1962 No 139 Squadron RAF became the first to be equipped with the improved Victor B.Mk 2, which first flew on 20 February 1959. Changes included the use of four 9344kg (20,600lb)st Rolls-Royce Conway R.Co.17 Mk 201 turbofan engines (then

Ex-Victor B.Mk 1A bomber converted into a flight refuelling tanker and seen here in the company of a Lightning interceptor.

Ninth Victor B.Mk 2 built with its crew. This aircraft participated in the development of reconnaissance mapping radar.

Blue Steel stand-off missiles prepared for Vulcan and Victor bombers.

known as by-pass turbojets), fitted in 36.58m (120ft) span and 241.3sq m (2597sq ft)-area wings. These changes allowed the maximum cruising altitude to be increased from 13,715m (45,000ft) for the B.Mk 1 to 16,765m (55,000ft), and combat radius at high altitude was 3701km (2300 miles). The air intakes for the engines were enlarged, retractable scoops to feed ram-air to the two turbo-alternators for emergency power supplies were fitted either side of the rear fuselage, and a dorsal fillet was added forward of the tailfin (which still carried its distinctive swept back tailplane with marked dihedral). Mk 2 aircraft were subsequently given streamlined fairings above the trailing-edges of the wings. These helped reduce drag at high speed and contained 'window' (chaff) dispensers to confuse radars. Perhaps the most identifiable

feature of the Victor in all versions was the design of its nose, with its large dielectric blister under the panel-glazed nose.

Production of the Victor B.Mk 2 totalled 34 aircraft, 21 being subsequently modified to carry the Blue Steel nuclear stand-off missile. The first squadron so equipped was No 139 in early 1964. Four years later the Victor finally passed out of service as a bomber. However, six B.Mk1As had previously become B(K).1A two-point flight refuelling tankers and a further 24 bombers were modified as K.Mk 1/1A three-point tankers. Also, nine B.Mk 2s had been adapted as strategic reconnaissance aircraft under the designation SR.Mk 2, serving with No 543 Squadron until replaced by Vulcans in 1974. On 8 May 1974 the first Victor K.Mk 2 three-point flight refueling tankers (with Mk 20 pods) entered RAF service, 24 being delivered by 1977. These were modified B.Mk 2s and SR.Mk 2s with wing span reduced to 35.66m (117ft) and

other changes. A valuable part of today's RAF, K.Mk 2 tankers operating during the Falkland Island campaign performed nearly 600 missions, of which all but one percent were entirely successful.

The earlier phase-out of bomber versions of the Valiant and Victor, and the planned withdrawal of the Vulcan in 1982, were expected to end more than a quarter of a century of V-bomber deployment by the RAF. As for the Canberra, this has no offensive role to play in today's RAF. A supersonic replacement had been designed and built to prototype stage as the TSR 2, but this was cancelled during the 1960s for economic reasons, although it was then by far the most formidable aircraft of its type in the world.

Ground crew prepare to load reconnaissance cameras on to a Victor SR.Mk 2.

12: THE NAVAL BOMBER

Because so few nations have deployed aircraft carriers postwar, the number of jet-powered aircraft built for the role of naval attack bomber has been small. Of these, only the United States has produced attack bombers of any size. This was made possible by the deployment by the US Navy of 'super-carriers.' Indeed, most naval bombers originated in the United States and this situation is likely to continue in the future as the US Navy deploys virtually all of the world's carriers suited to non-VTOL aircraft.

Two manufacturers were paramount in supplying early jet bomber/attack aircraft to Navy requirements, namely North American and Douglas. To the former company went the honor of supplying the first postwar carrier-borne attack bomber incorporating turbojet engines, in the shape of the AJ Savage. This aircraft also gave the US Navy its first capability to delivery atomic weapons.

Development of the Savage was initiated in 1946, with the first XAJ-1 prototype flying on 3 July 1948. A three seater with pressurized accommodation, it was powered by two 2400hp Pratt & Whitney R-2800-44W piston engines in nacelles under the shoulder-mounted unswept but tapering wings and a 2086kg (4600lb)st Allison J33 turbojet engine installed in the rear fuselage. For cruise flight only the piston engines were expected to be used, the turbojet providing extra power for take-off and for increasing speed in combat. The prototype demonstrated more than 740km/h (460mph).

Production of the Savage for the Navy began with 43 AJ-1s, differing mainly in the standard use of wingtip tanks. The first production AJ-1 flew in May 1949 and the type entered service a few months later. Approximately 5440kg (12,000lb) of conventional bombs or a nuclear weapon could be carried in the bomb bay. With the arrival of the improved AJ-2 versions, many AJ-1s were modified into flight refueling tankers, using the probe and drogue system. A pack containing the necessary equipment for this role was installed in the bomb bay.

The AJ-2 and AJ-2P followed the AJ-1 into service, changes including the use of R-2800-48 piston engines and the turbojet, a taller fin and rudder of increased area, a tailplane without the dihedral of the AJ-1 and increased fuel. The first production version was the AJ-2P photographic reconnaissance aircraft, carrying cameras in a redesigned and more bulbous nose for day and night photography at all altitudes. Photo-flash bombs were carried in the bomb bay. The first AJ-2P flew on 6 March 1952 and production was ended in 1954.

The AJ-2 attack bomber followed the AJ-2P, the first aircraft flying on 19 February 1953. However, this version too was soon

Previous page: Douglas A-4F Skyhawk flown by the US Marine Corps, with a J52-P-8A engine and improved avionics carried in a dorsal hump.

North American AJ-2 Savage naval attack bomber.

Douglas A3D-2 Skywarrior converted into an EKA-3B for service in Vietnam with Tactical Electronics Warfare Squadron VAQ-135.

being modified for the tanker role. In September 1962, under the new designation system which rationalized US military aircraft designations, surviving Savage aircraft took A-2 designations. An attempt to modernize the design had previously been made with the introduction of a prototype with Allison T40 turboprop engines under the wings in place of the former piston engines. This resulted in the XA2J-1 prototype. In fact this was a completely redesigned aircraft, with a new slimmer fuselage and new cockpit, a more modern tailplane, and with provision for radar-controlled 20mm cannon in the tail. This did not enter production.

1956 was a significant year for the US Navy and its future attack capability. In April of that year the first of its big Skywarrior attack bombers entered service, followed in October by the first of its small Skyhawks. Both were from Douglas and both had a major impact on Navy capabilities.

The Skywarrior was a bold concept, designed to provide the US Navy with an aircraft of tremendous speed and range and large enough to carry the heaviest conventional bombs or deliver nuclear weapons. It proved capable of high or low level attack, and eventually encompassed photographic reconnaissance and mine-laying roles, and yet could be launched from and retrieved by aircraft carriers.

The events that made development of the Skywarrior possible dated from World War II, when the US Navy commissioned the first of its new *Essex* class of 'supercarriers.' *Essex* was followed immediately after the war by the *Midway* class and then by the *Forrestal* class. These huge vesels in service or planned would, it was decided, allow the operation of much heavier aircraft if sufficiently powerful engines could be installed. While Savage attack bombers were being constructed, but before any had reached operational units, an order was place with Douglas for two prototypes of its A3D-1 Skywarrior. This attack bomber was to be far larger and heavier than anything built previously for carrier operations. The first prototype flew initially on 28 October 1952 on the power of two pod-mounted Westinghouse J40 turbojets. This engine had been flight tested for the first time only the previous year and had been selected for being then the most powerful turbojet of US manufacture.

Production of the Skywarrior began with 50 A3D-1s, the first of which were delivered in March 1956 and joined the fleet in 1957. Because of development problems with the Westinghouse engine, each A3D-1 had two more powerful Pratt & Whitney J57-P-6 tur-

bojets installed below the shoulder-mounted swept wings. Production of J57s had started in February 1953, just in time to power the first service test A3D-1.

In early 1957 the Pacific Fleet received the first of 164 improved A3D-2s. Each A3D-2 was powered by J57-P-10 turbojets and had a modified 4.57m (15ft) bomb-bay to allow the carriage of a greater variety of weapons. As with the A3D-1, the crew comprised a pilot, co-pilot/bombardier (seated by the pilot) and rear-facing navigator/gunner. Defensive armament was the usual twin 20mm cannon in the rear fuselage, mounted in a Westinghouse Aero 21-B ball turret and radar directed. This version had a maximum take-off weight of 37,195kg (82,000lb), making it the heaviest aircraft ever operated from aircraft carriers, and a maximum speed of 982km/h (610mph) at 3050m (10,000ft). Range was more than 4667km (2900 miles). In 1962 A3Ds were redesignated A-3s. As a small number of A3D-1s had been converted into trial photographic reconnaissance and electronic-countermeasures aircraft, so actual production versions were produced based on the A3D-2. The A3D-2P (later RA-3B) was the photographic-reconnaissance version carrying 12 cameras in a strengthened and completely pressurized fuselage. Length was reduced from 23.27m (76ft 4in) to 23.01m (75ft 6in) and tail armament was retained. The first of 30 flew on 22 July 1958. The A3D-2Q (later EA-3B) was the ECM

Douglas A3D-2 Skywarriors converted as KA-3Bs for operation by squadron VAK-208.

variant, the crew comprising seven persons (four specialists accommodated in a bomb-bay cabin). Twenty-four were produced, the first flying on 10 December 1958. Another variant appeared in 1959 as the A3D-2T navigator and bombardier trainer, accommodating a pilot, an instructor and six pupils. Twelve were built, becoming TA-3Bs in 1962.

By the early 1960s the Skywarrier was at

A-4G Skyhawk, a version of the A-4F for the Royal Australian Air Force and equipped to carry Sidewinder missiles if required.

the peak of its service, equipping no less than 18 Navy squadrons. But rapidly the Navy's strategic power was taken away from aircraft carriers and put in less vulnerable submarines, the role of the Skywarrior and deck or ramp-launched Regulus missiles diminishing accordingly. During the Vietnam conflict Skywarriors found new roles, firstly as KA-3B flight refueling tankers and then EKA-3B tanker/counter-measures or strike (TACOS) aircraft, 30 of the latter being produced by conversion. In the early 1980s the US Navy still had EA-3Bs, KA-3Bs and TA-3Bs listed as operational, a total of 58 aircraft.

The second production A3D-1 Skywarrior on display by two other new aircraft, the XB-51 and Douglas C-124 Globemaster II transport.

The small Skyhawk, originally with the A4D designations but from 1962 known as the A-4, was the logical progression of the prewar Devastator, wartime Dauntless and postwar Skyraider, all of which were piston engined. Ordered in prototype form in 1952, Douglas had been able to assess the role of Navy light attack Skyraiders fighting in Korea and the success of jet fighters seen in widespread combat for the first time. The

The last of 2,960 Skyhawks built was this A-4M Skyhawk II.

outcome was the design of a single-seat lightweight aircraft suited to all sizes of aircraft carriers and operation from land. Its configuration was that of a tailed delta, with a wing leading-edge sweepback of 33 degrees.

Construction of the XA4D-1 prototype started in September 1953 and it made its

The USMC's OA-4M forward air control Skyhawk.

maiden flight on the power of a 3265kg (7200lb)st Wright J65-W-2 turbojet engine installed in the rear fuselage on 22 June 1954. Nineteen service test YA4D-1s followed. Actual production began with the A4D-1, fitted with the more powerful 3538kg (7800lb)st J65-W-4 turbojet. The first production aircraft flew initially on 14 August 1954 and the first of 146 entered service with the Atlantic and Pacific Fleets in October 1956. Under the 1962 military designation system, this version became the A-4A.

By the end of production in early 1979, no fewer than 2405 combat Skyhawks and a

further 555 tandem two-seat trainers had been built for the US Navy, Marine Corps and for the forces of many other countries. Of the 17 production versions, the A4D-2 (A-4B) with a J65-W-16A turbojet, the A4D-2N (A-4C) with a longer nose to house additional radar for improved all-weather capabilities, the longer-range A4D-5 (A-4E) with a 3855kg (8500lb)st Pratt & Whitney J52-P-6A turbojet and ability to carry an increased weapon-load of 3720kg (8200lb), and the TA-4J trainer were the most produced, with 542, 638, 494 and 291 completed respectively. The A-4M, 162 of which were built, was the first of the improved Skyhawk IIs, powered by a 5080kg (11,200lb)st J52-P408A turbojet. This has a maximum take-off weight of 11,113kg (24,500lb), a maximum speed of 1038km/h (645mph) while carrying a 1814kg (4000lb) warload and a ferry range of 3307km (2055 miles). Total weapon load is 4536kg (10,000lb), which can include conventional and nuclear bombs, missiles, rockets and many other stores. Two wing-mounted cannon are standard.

US Skyhawks were operated widely during the Vietnam conflict. Most recently those in Argentine service took part in the hostilities over the Falkland Islands, their most important victory coming with the sinking of the Royal Navy Type 42 destroyer HMS *Coventry* on 25 May 1982. Between these conflicts Skyhawks of other nations had seen action. Of course other versions of the Skyhawk have been produced by con-

version, the latest being the USMC's OA-4M, 23 of which were being prepared from two-seat TA-4Fs for forward air control missions.

The aircraft selected to follow on from the Skywarrior as the Navy's heavy attack bomber was the North American A3J Vigilante. This was designed to provide the US Navy with a Mach 2 aircraft of the highest caliber, equal to any land-based attack bomber in the world. A two-seater, its weapon load provided for the carriage of nuclear and conventional bombs in a unique 'linear' bomb-bay plus underwing stores. The bomb-bay comprised a tunnel with rollers inside the rear fuselage, on which bombs could be positioned and later ejected between the engine jetpipes. LABS (low-altitude bombing system) or 'toss' bombing could be employed.

The Vigilante was designed as a high-wing attack bomber with a wing sweepback on the leading-edge of 37 degrees. Hydraulically-actuated variable-camber leading-edges were fitted in three sections to each wing. Spoilers and underwing deflectors were fitted instead of the usual ailerons, plus flaps. The wings folded to aid on-board stowage.

Prototypes were ordered in 1956 and the first of two took to the air for the first time on 31 August 1958. The A3J-1 (later A-5A) initial production version was, in the event, the only attack bomber, entering service in 1961 and first becoming operational on board the new USS Enterprise the following year. Enterprise was the US Navy's first nuclear-powered aircraft carrier and the largest warship in the world. Early Vigilantes had two 4695kg (10,350lb)st dry General Electric J79-GE-4 turbojet engines with afterburners installed side by side in the rear fuselage, but these gave way to 4944kg (10,900lb)st dry-rated J79-GE-8s. Production totalled 57 aircraft plus the two prototypes.

A long-range attack bomber had been planned as the follow-on A3J-2 (A-5B), extra fuel being carried in a humped fairing above the fuselage. However, by then Navy deployment plans for the future did not include a requirement for such an aircraft, or indeed the use of an attack bomber of A3J-1 caliber. Therefore, the six initial A3J-2s were modified on the production line into A3J-3s (RA-5Cs) reconnaissance aircraft.

The RA-5C was first flown on 30 June 1962 and yet remained operational until re-

TA-4J two-seat trainer version of the Skyhawk, in service with the US Navy.

The North American Vigilante was the most powerful attack aircraft operated from aircraft carriers, second in size and weight only to the Savage. Here RA-5C reconnaissance aircraft are illustrated, the last Vigilantes in service.

Grumman A-6E/TRAM Intruder, the US Navy's latest version of this carrier-based attack aircraft.

cently. It was conceived as the airborne component of the Integrated Operational Intelligence System, carrying for its main reconnaissance role tactical sensors and cameras in a long underfuselage fairing. Other items of equipment included side-looking radar and electro-magnetic sensors for countermeasures (ECM) and intelligence gathering. Engines comprised either J79-GE-8s or later 5395kg (11,870lb)st dry J79-GE-10s, bestowing a take-off weight for a normal reconnaissance mission of 30,300kg (66,800lb), a maximum speed of 2228km/h (1385mph), a service ceiling of 15240m (50,000ft) and a range of 4830km (3000 miles). Maximum weight of this version was 36,100kg (79,587lb). The four underwing attachment points for auxiliary fuel tanks could also carry weapons. RA-5Cs were first delivered to the US Navy's training squadron for Heavy Attack Wing One in 1964. The aircraft first became operational on board USS *Ranger* in the South China Sea, equipping Reconnaissance Attack Squadron 5. By 1965 the attack bomber version of the Vigilante had given way completely to the reconnaissance model and eventually Heavy Attack Wing One became known as Reconnaissance Attack Wing One. Further RA-5Cs were built thereafter.

The US Navy's 'A' series for attack aircraft designation covered many varying types, examples already mentioned including lightweight and heavy, medium and long-range, single and multi-engined, and single-seat and multi-seat aircraft. In 1957 Grumman was selected winner of a competition for a new carrier-borne low-level attack bomber, expected to locate and attack enemy targets in all weather conditions and in darkness at long range, and carry a wide variety and heavy load of conventional and nuclear weapons. High subsonic performance was accepted as the most suitable for this penetration role.

The Grumman attack bomber was originally designated A2F-1 Intruder (later A-6 under the 1962 system), the first flying on 19 April 1960. This was one of four initial development aircraft ordered for 1960 and was to be followed by four more in 1961. It was a mid-wing aircraft with just 25 degrees of sweepback at quarter chord, accommodating a crew of two on slightly staggered side-by-side ejection seats. Five attachment points each had a capacity of 1633kg

(3600lb), and could carry many combinations of weapons including 30 500lb bombs or Bullpup missiles. Deliveries to VA-42 at NAS Oceana began in February 1963 and the last was accepted in December 1969. A total of 482 was completed for the Navy and Marine Corps. These were widely employed during the Vietnam conflict.

Six converted A-6As subsequently joined 27 newly-built EA-6A Intruders for the new electronic reconnaissance and ECM role, the prototype of which appeared in 1963. A much refined version of the EA-6A subsequently appeared as the EA-6B Prowler. A-6B was the designation of nineteen A-6As modified to carry Standard ARM

anti-radiation missiles, to provide the capability of destroying enemy defensive and missile guidance radars. A-6C applied to 12 A-6As modified to carry forward-looking infra-red sensors and low light television camera for night attack.

In 1966 a modified A-6A flew as the KA-6D tanker and 62 were produced in this way. The only new-production version has come in the form of the advanced A-6E Intruder of 1970, carrying multi-mode radar and an IBM computer. Operational since 1972, a total of 318 was expected originally, many produced by converting A-6As but the remainder as new construction. Production was continuing in 1982. A version of the

A-6E with target recognition and attack multisensor equipment first appeared in 1974 as the A-6E/TRAM. This variant can carry laser-guided weapons and first went to sea operationally in 1980. Eventually all A-6Es will have this capability. Maximum take-off weight for the A-6E when operating from an aircraft carrier is 26,580kg (58,600lb), maximum speed is 1037km/h (644mph) and range 5222km (3245 miles). Maximum weapon load is 8165kg (18,000lb), made possible by two 4218kg (9300lb)st Pratt & Whitney J52-P-8B turbojet engines.

Grumman Intruder, Prowler (2nd aircraft) and other types on board USS *John F. Kennedy* in 1978.

A-7As on board USS *Midway* in 1975, operated by VA-93.

In 1964 the US Navy announced that LTV had won a competition for a single-seat, carrier-based light attack aircraft designed as a subsonic replacement for the Skyhawk. Later known as the A-7 Corsair II, it had been based on the company's earlier F-8 Crusader fighter, although shorter in length and without the fighter's unusual wing. The first development aircraft flew initially on 27 September 1965. In 1967 A-7A production aircraft became operational, immediately going into action over Vietnam.

The A-7A used a non-afterburning Pratt & Whitney TF30-P-6 turbofan engine with a

thrust of 5148kg (11,350lb). A total of 199 was built. Follow-on versions were built for the Navy, plus land-based A-7Ds, with Allison TF41-A-1 engines for the USAF and A-7Hs for the Hellenic Air Force, and two-seat trainers. Portugal has also received A-7Ps, which are refurbished A-7As. The last Navy version was built as the A-7E for attack, close support and interdiction, which went out of production in 1981 after 596 had been built. Powered by a 6803kg (15,000lb)st Allison TF 41-A-2 turbofan, it can carry more than 6803kg (15,000lb) of weapons on eight

Above: USAF A-7D armed with fifteen 750lb general-purpose bombs.

An LTV A-7A Corsair II of VA-147, taking off carrying Snakeye bombs. VA-147 was the first operational A-7 squadron.

Above: *XK490,* one of the first twenty Buccaneer S.Mk 1s for the Royal Navy, seen flying over a Folland Gnat during a Farnborough air display.

external stations. Maximum take-off weight is 19,050kg (42,000lb), maximum speed 1112km/h (691mph) and maximum ferry range 4604km (2861 miles).

A French-built, carrier-borne aircraft that caused much damage to British Task Force vessels during the recent conflict over the Falkland Islands is the Dassault-Breguet Super Etendard. Carrying Exocet anti-shipping missiles, Argentinian Super Etendards operated from the mainland. However, as the Super Etendard is a Mach 1 strike fighter and can carry air-to-air armament as well as bombs, rockets and other missiles (French Navy aircraft also have provision for tactical nuclear weapons), it was included in *Jet Fighters.*

Until HMS *Ark Royal* was scrapped, the Royal Navy operated the two-seat carrier-borne low-level Hawker Siddeley Buccaneer strike aircraft. Others were in service with the RAF and South African Air Force as land-based aircraft. It was the former of these that took over naval Buccaneers when the Royal Navy became a V/STOL fixed-wing aircraft force operating Sea Harriers, and these continue in service.

Originating as the Blackburn B.103 and conforming to Naval Specification NA 39, the Buccaneer was first flown on 30 April

Buccaneer S.Mk 1 on board a Royal Navy aircraft carrier.

French Navy Dassault-Breguet Super Etendard, one of the most widely known naval aircraft following its use by Argentina during the Falklands conflict. This Super Etendard carries an Exocet.

1958. The first version was the Royal Navy S.Mk 1, with two 3220kg (7100lb)st Bristol Siddeley Gyron Junior turbojet engines housed in nacelles on each side of the fuselage. The mid-mounted wings were swept at 40 degrees at the root. The first of forty production S.Mk 1s flew on 23 January 1962 and No 801 Squadron (the first Navy Buccaneer squadron) embarked on board HMS *Ark Royal* in early 1963.

The Buccaneer S.Mk 2 was the developed version with Rolls-Royce RB.168 Spey turbofan engines and extended wing-tips, production aircraft appearing from

1964. A total of 84 was built, entering Royal Navy service from 1965. Royal Navy Buccaneers later became known as S.Mk 2Cs and S.Mk 2Ds, the latter designation indicating a capability to carry Martel air-to-surface missiles. Meanwhile, Buccaneer production for the RAF had begun, No 12 Squadron becoming the first operational RAF unit with the S.Mk 2B in 1970. This version was given Martel capability and 43 operational examples were built as new. As the Royal Navy disposed of its Buccaneers, so many became RAF S.Mk 2As (without the ability to carry Martel) and S.Mk 2Bs. The RAF's Buccaneers with 5035kg (11,100lb)st RB.168-1A Spey Mk 101 turbofans can carry a weapon load of up to 7257kg (16,000lb). Maximum speed at 60m (200ft) altitude is 1038km/h (646mph) and range for a typical sortie is 3700km (2300 miles).

RAF Buccaneers of No 12 Squadron at Gibraltar during a NATO exercise.

RAF Buccaneer S.Mk 2B capable of carrying Martel air-to-surface missiles.

255

13: WIELDING THE BIG STICK

By the late 1940s both the United States and the Soviet Union had developed multi-engined jet bombers well suited to tactical roles. But political divisions around the world demanded that the same type of modern powerplant be applied at the earliest possible time to strategic bombers with intercontinental range.

Turbojet engines capable of producing high thrust were available. The main problem was that while a sufficient number of turbojet engines matched to a high-technology airframe could produce an aircraft with good speed and weapon carrying capability, no such guarantees could be given for range. Despite great advances in design and development since the war, turbojets were still very fuel thirsty.

One answer was not to adopt turbojet engines for a jet bomber but turboprops and it was on this type of engine that both nations originally conceived strategic jet bombers. Prior to the USAF receiving production versions of the Boeing B-50 and Convair B-36 piston-engined strategic bombers, Boeing proposed an entirely new aircraft with straight wings and six Wright XT35 turboprop engines. The XT35 was then under development and was expected to produce 5500shp. Flight testing of the engine mounted in the nose of one of two B-17Gs used by the Wright Aeronautical Corporation as Model 2997Zs began in September 1947, by which time the 1946 proposal had been modified to incorporate swept wings following a visit to Germany by Boeing engineers. This new configuration appeared to offer a high performance and good range and in July 1948 Boeing received a contract to build two prototypes of its Model 464 for the USAF.

Meanwhile Boeing had flown and tested its prototype B-47 Stratojet medium bomber. The excellence of this with its 35 degrees of wing sweepback and six turbojet engines convinced the company that a similar approach was feasible for the Model 464. With the agreement of the USAF, the Model 464 were redesigned to incorporate a sweep of 35 degrees and eight 3946kg (8700lb)st Pratt & Whitney J57-P-1W turbojet engines carried in pairs on underwing pylons. In this configuration and with a B-47-style bubble canopy for the pilot and co-pilot in tandem, the two aircraft ordered were built, one as the XB-52 and the second as the YB-52 Stratofortress. The first to fly was the YB-52, taking to the air for the first time on 15 April 1952. The XB-52 followed on 2 October of the same year.

The initial production variant was the B-52A, powered by J57-P-9W engines. The

A Boeing B-52C flying over snow-capped mountains while en route to the Boeing Flight Center at Moses Lake, Washington, for flight trials prior to delivery to the USAF.

Previous page: A B-52G releases an air-launched cruise missile during development trials.

This view of the Boeing YB-52 shows clearly the tandem arrangement for the pilot and co-pilot under a bubble canopy.

most obvious external change to the prototypes was the new stepped cockpit for side-by-side accommodation of the pilot and co-pilot. Thirteen of these were to be built, but in the event only three were completed. The first flew initially on 5 August 1954. The remaining 10 from the first order were included in the total of 50 B-52Bs completed. In fact the 'B' was built in two subvariants, the standard B-52B and the RB-52B with strategic bombing capability and the ability to carry a pressurized and manned capsule in the bomb-bay for strategic photographic reconnaissance and electronic countermeasures roles. Powered by J57-P-19W, -29W or -29WA turbojets, 23 B-52Bs and 27 RB-52Bs were completed.

Above: B-52D Stratofortress about to refuel from a USAF Boeing KC-135A Stratotanker.

A mock-up of the new non-nuclear
General Dynamics AGM-109H
Tomahawk II cruise missile is displayed
in front of a B-52D at March AFB.

Boeing B-52F releases fifty-one 750 lb bombs over a target in South Vietnam.

One of six B-52s, from the 5th and 39th Bomb Wings that flew non-stop from North Dakota to Egypt and back during exercise Bright Star 82, dropping 500lb retarded bombs.

The 500lb retarded bombs explode on the desert sand.

One each of the first two production versions were subsequently set aside from their strategic role and converted to be NB-52A and NB-52B 'motherplanes' for the air-launched North American X-15 hypersonic aircraft research program, taking off with an X-15 under a wing for the first time on 10 March 1959. Meanwhile other versions of the Stratofortress had entered production. The B-52C was first flown on 9 March 1956. Thirty-five were eventually built with 4536kg (10,000lb)st J57-P-29W engines. The B-52D was first flown on 4 June 1956 and 170 were eventually completed with -19W or -29W engines. The B-52E with improved bombing, electronics and nagivation systems was flown on 3 October 1957 and 100 were built, followed by the B-52F 89 of which were completed with -43W engines of 6237kg (13,750lb)st.

The B-52G was the major production version of the Stratofortress, 193 of which were built between 1958 and 1961. Developed from the 'F,' it had a greatly increased range largely thanks to its redesigned wings with integral fuel tanks, a shorter tail fin and rud-

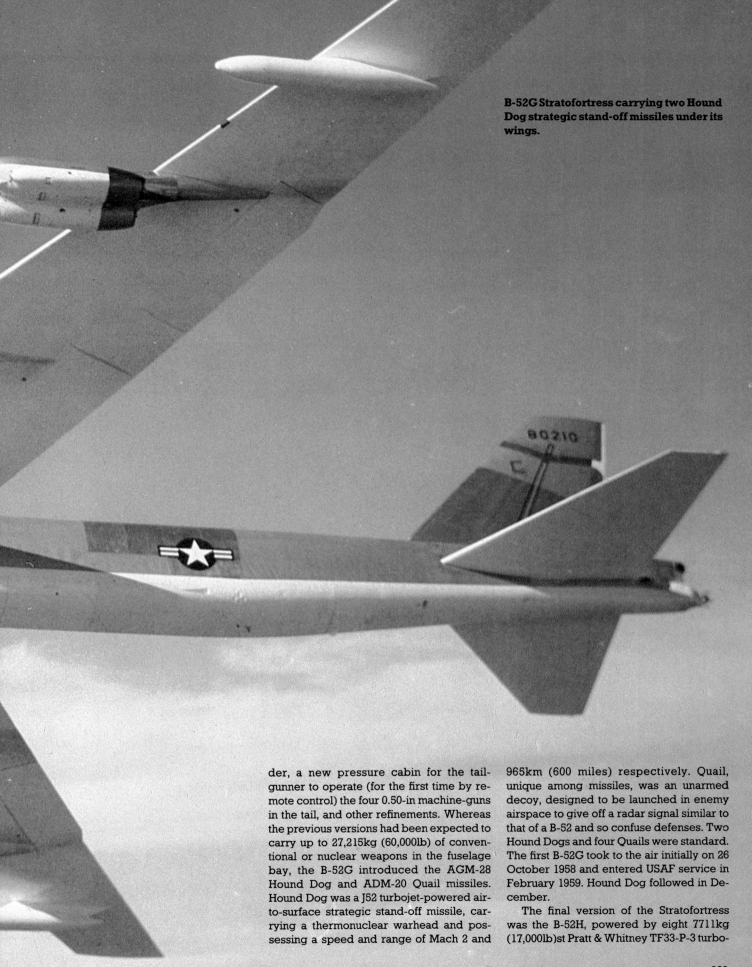

B-52G Stratofortress carrying two Hound Dog strategic stand-off missiles under its wings.

der, a new pressure cabin for the tail-gunner to operate (for the first time by remote control) the four 0.50-in machine-guns in the tail, and other refinements. Whereas the previous versions had been expected to carry up to 27,215kg (60,000lb) of conventional or nuclear weapons in the fuselage bay, the B-52G introduced the AGM-28 Hound Dog and ADM-20 Quail missiles. Hound Dog was a J52 turbojet-powered air-to-surface strategic stand-off missile, carrying a thermonuclear warhead and possessing a speed and range of Mach 2 and

965km (600 miles) respectively. Quail, unique among missiles, was an unarmed decoy, designed to be launched in enemy airspace to give off a radar signal similar to that of a B-52 and so confuse defenses. Two Hound Dogs and four Quails were standard. The first B-52G took to the air initially on 26 October 1958 and entered USAF service in February 1959. Hound Dog followed in December.

The final version of the Stratofortress was the B-52H, powered by eight 7711kg (17,000lb)st Pratt & Whitney TF33-P-3 turbo-

Above: Between the fuselage of this B-52H and each inboard pair of engines are carried two Skybolt missiles.

Right: The final production version of the Stratofortress was the B-52H. This B-52H is not carrying any external stores, although the single 20mm Vulcan multi-barrel tail cannon can be seen.

fan engines. This version was expected to carry the Skybolt strategic missile and had a 20mm Vulcan multibarrel cannon in the tail. When Skybolt was cancelled, it reverted to Hound Dogs and Quails. Production totalled 102, the first flying on 6 March 1961. The final B-52 Stratofortress, a B-52H, appeared in mid-1962 and joined the USAF in October. This, with the 'G', is the heaviest version, at a maximum take-off weight of more than 221,350kg (488,000lb). Maximum speed is 957km/h (595mph) and unrefueled range is more than 16,093km (10,000 miles).

Stratofortress carried out many missions

Right: B-52G Stratofortress with its external load of twelve SRAM missiles visible under the wings.

with heavy loads of conventional bombs during the Vietnam conflict, operating from Guam and Thailand. Thereafter, and with the first of its expected replacement bombers already cancelled, it underwent the first of several rebuilding programs to allow extended service. Two hundred and eighty-one "G"s and "H"s were eventually rearmed with SRAMs (Short Range Attack Missiles), each B-52 carrying eight in the bomb-bay on a rotary launcher and 12 under the wings, plus free-fall nuclear bombs. Other programs have introduced many new electronic and other systems. Very recently the first of an expected total of 173 B-52Gs reentered USAF service equipped to carry and launch 12 AGM-86B cruise missiles, in addition to internally-carried SRAMs and bombs. B-52Hs may also be similarly converted at a future date. Currently the USAF has 347 Stratofortresses in operational service, comprising 269 B-52Gs and Hs and 78 B-52Ds. Whether these remain operational until the end of the century to be the first combat aircraft in aviation history to complete 45 years of first-line service will have to be seen. It largely depends on the deployment of the B-1B replacement.

Top: Eight SRAM missiles on their rotary launcher being prepared for the bomb-bay of a B-52G.

Above: The latest missile developed for the B-52 is the Boeing AGM-86B air-launched cruise missile. Here twelve are carried during development trials.

In 1946 the Soviet Union produced the first examples of its Tupolev Tu-4. Subsequently known to NATO as *Bull,* it was based on the US piston-engined Boeing B-29. By the latter 1940s it had become clear that a successor was required urgently. Among those proposed were the Tupolev Tu-80 and refined Tu-85. Both were based on the Tu-4 and retained piston engines. Prototypes appeared in 1949 but these were not what was needed, and Stalin for one let this be known. However, already early work on

turbojet-powered Tu-4 replacements were in design and, while waiting for these would mean delay, the prospect of the increased performance was persuasive.

Two main contenders for the smaller twin-engined replacement were produced as prototypes, the Ilyushin Il-46 and the Tupolev Tu-88 first flying in 1952. The former was an enlarged derivative of the successful Il-28. Considering the backing that the Il-28 had received from Stalin, Ilyushin must have been confident of success. This was not to be the case. The Tu-88 was a much more modern aircraft, perhaps surprisingly so considering Tupolev's earlier proposals. Roughly in the class of the US Boeing B-47 Stratojet but even more advanced, it had swept back wings and tail surfaces and two large but simple high-thrust Mikulin AM-3 axial-flow engines semi-recessed into the fuselage.

As the Tu-16, the bomber was selected for service and entered production in 1953. This first production variant was given the reporting name *Badger-A* by NATO and took part in the May Day flypast of 1954. It was a strategic bomber, with a stepped cockpit for the pilot and co-pilot and a glazed nose for the navigator. The three other crew members were gunner/observers. A small radome was housed under the nose. Defensive armament comprised 7 23mm NR 23 cannon in nose, dorsal, ventral and tail positions. Bombload was an impressive 9000kg (19,842lb).

Before production ended in the Soviet Union in the 1960s, it is thought likely that approximately 2000 were built. Identified versions with their NATO reporting names that followed *Badger-A* were the *Badger-B*

bomber carrying two *Kennel* 100km (63 mile) range antishipping missiles; *Badger-C* antishipping aircraft carrying either *Kipper* or later *Kingfish* nuclear or conventional missiles; *Badger-D* maritime and electronic reconnaissance aircraft with a larger undernose radome and other fairing for electronic equipment; *Badger-E* photographic reconnaissance aircraft; *Badger-F* photographic reconnaissance and electronic intelligence aircraft; *Badger-G* bomber with *Kelt* 160km (100 mile) range stand-off missiles or *Kingfish* and conventional or nuclear bombs; *Badger-H* and *Badger-J* ECM jamming aircraft to escort and protect armed aircraft; and *Badger-K* electronic reconnaissance aircraft.

Badger has a take-off weight of approximately 72,000kg (158,730lb). Its maximum

level speed on the power of two 8750kg (19,290lb)st AM-3 engines is 992km/h (616mph) and range with a 3790kg (8360lb) bombload is 4800km (3000 miles). Later aircraft were installed with more powerful 9500kg (20,944lb)st RD-3M turbojets.

Today it is believed that just over 800 *Badgers* remain in service with the Soviet Dalnaya Aviatsiya (long range air force) and Naval Aviation. These include *Badger-Bs*, now without missiles but carrying nuclear or conventional bombs, other strategic and strike versions and approximately 125 air force and 110 naval ECM, reconnaissance and flight refueling tanker aircraft. In addition, Egypt and Iraq deploy bombers and China operates approximately 100 as locally-built Xian H-6s. Production in China continues.

An Egyptian Air Force Tupolev Tu-16 *Badger* bomber armed with a *Kelt* air-to-surface stand-off missile.

Inset: Soviet Naval Aviation Tu-16 *Badger* on a maritime reconnaissance mission.

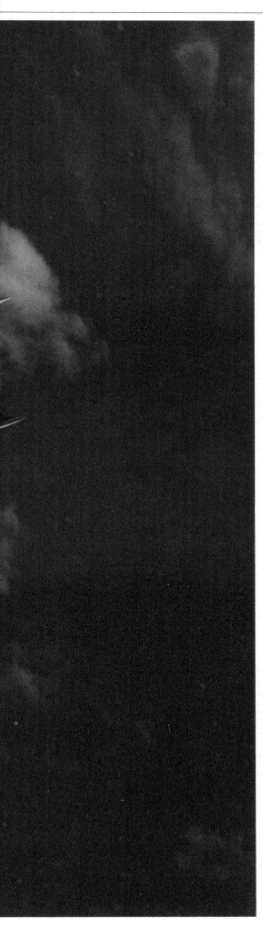

Above: Soviet Naval Aviation Myasishchev M-4 *Bison-C*.

Left: This view of a Soviet *Bear* gives a good indication of its configuration.

True intercontinental strategic capability came to the Soviet Union with the development of the Myasishchev M-4 and Tupolev Tu-95, known to NATO by the reporting names *Bison* and *Bear*. These were developed as 'heavies' to complement the much lighter and less formidable Tu-16 and as such were as much Tu-4 replacements. Superficially the M-4 and Tu-95 were similar, both having wings with approximately 37 degrees of sweepback and swept tail surfaces. However, there was a fundamental difference between the two aircraft, which was to rob the M-4 of the oper-

Soviet Dalnaya Aviatsiya Tupolev Tu-95 *Bear-B* long-range bomber carrying under its fuselage a large *Kangaroo* air-to-surface strategic missile.

ational performance enjoyed by the Tu-95.

One of the most important requirements for new bombers was that of extremely long range, sometimes quoted at 16,000km (9942 miles). The first of the two aircraft to appear was the Myasishchev M-4, the design of which had been completed is 1952 and the prototype flew over Moscow during the May Day flypast exactly two years later. It was powered by four Mikulin AM-3D turbojets carried as podded pairs in the wing roots, each rated at 8700kg (19,180lb)st.

The first version, which was the first Soviet production four-turbojet bomber, was given the reporting name *Bison-A* by NATO. This was a bomber carrying conventional or nuclear free-fall bombs. Although possessing a good maximum speed for a huge aircraft of this period – 1000km/h (620mph) – it range fell well short of that required and is now estimated at 8000km (4971 miles) while carrying a 5500kg (12125lb) bombload. Its service ceiling was also disappointing at only about 13,700m (45,000ft), necessitating a defensive arma-

A Soviet Naval Aviation Tu-142 Bear-D being escorted back to sea by an RAF Lightning interceptor of No 23 Squadron.

ment of 10 23mm cannon. Maximum take-off weight (estimated, as are the other figures quoted) is 158,750kg (350,000lb). Today the Dalnaya Aviatsiya still includes approximately 45 M-4s in bomber configuration, and a further 35 are thought to be used as flight refueling tankers.

Two other versions of the M-4 were produced for Soviet Naval Aviation. *Bison-B* and *Bison-C* were maritime reconnaissance-bombers, with solid noses replacing *Bison-A's* hemispherical, lightly-glazed nose and other changes including reduced armament. *Bison-C* was the heaviest of all M-4 versions and possessed the highest performance, its maximum speed being estimated at 1060km/h (658mph) and service ceiling at 15,600m (51,180ft). Neither maritime version is thought to be operational.

Bear-F photographed as it is being escorted away by USAF Phantom II fighters in September 1980.

Far more significant to the Soviet air forces is the Tupolev Tu-95, which first flew as a prototype in the latter part of 1954 and could be seen in the sky over Tushino in July of the following year. Unlike the M-4, this aircraft had been designed to use four huge turboprop engines driving contrarotating propellers, these being 14,795shp Kuznetsov NK-12MVs. The engine was then, and is still, the most powerful turboprop ever built, its development being aided by German engineers working in the Soviet Union. It has a 14-stage axial-flow compressor and has a dry weight of 2350kg (5,181lb). Incredibly, because of the excellence of this engine, both this and the Tu-95 are still built today to maintain the number of operational aircraft.

The first version of the Tu-95 to enter service with the long range air force was given the reporting name *Bear-A* by NATO. This is a strategic bomber with a maximum speed of 925km/h (575mph) and a maximum range while carrying a full load of 11,340kg (25,000lb) of conventional or nuclear weapons of 12,550km (7800 miles). It carries six 23mm cannon for defense. The *Bear-B* and *C* were first seen in the early 1960s and

carry as their primary armament either a 650km (400mile) range *Kangaroo* or 300km (185 mile) range *Kitchen* supersonic missile, designed to carry out strategic and stand-off attacks on surface targets. *Bear-C* is operated by Naval Aviation and as such carries the type designation Tu-142.

Bear-D differs from previous versions of *Bear* in so much as its main role with Naval Aviation is to relay targeting information to missile-carrying aircraft and ships. For this purpose it carries an X-band radar housed in an underfuselage radome and various other items of equipment in smaller fairings. *Bear-E* is a naval maritime reconnaissance aircraft with up to seven camera windows, and *Bear-F* is a naval antisubmarine strike aircraft.

Despite the continuing deployment of the supersonic Tu-22M *Backfire, Bear* remains vitally important to both the Dalnaya Aviatsiya and Naval Aviation, which operate approximately 109 and 95 respectively. However, with the development of the latest Soviet strategic bomber, the extremely formidable Mach 2.3 *Blackjack,* the longserving and versatile *Bear's* days could be numbered.

14: ATTACK

While the first jet bombers were appearing in the United States, thought was also being given to smaller jet-powered attack aircraft. In many respects these were designed to fulfill a role initiated by the Douglas XB-43 and, like its predecessor, at first carried 'A' (attack) Air Force designations.

After the A-42, which became the XB-42, came numerically the Curtiss A-43. This designation was applied to a side-by-side two-seat all-weather aircraft powered by four

Previous page: RAF SEPECAT Jaguar GR.Mk 1s sweep out to sea at low level.

Martin XB-51 three-jet attack bomber.

Westinghouse J34-engines that subsequently became the XF-87 fighter. This was first flown in February 1948. The A-44 was the original designation of what became the XB-53, a bold design by Convair for a light attack bomber of high performance, which unlike the XF-87 was never built. Development funds for the XA-44 were in fact drawn from the XB-46 project and two prototypes were ordered.

The XA-44/XB-53 was a most interesting design, probably the first in the United States to incorporate the swept forward wings originated in wartime Germany. These wings, with a sweep of 30 degrees and 8 degrees of dihedral, were to be

mounted on the rear fuselage. A fin and rudder only comprised the tail unit. Three General Electric J35 turbojets were carried inside the broad fuselage, an air intake being positioned each side of the fuselage. In attack configuration the aircraft carried a crew of two and the fuselage nose was solid. Armament was expected to comprise no less than 20 0.50in guns, and maximum speed and range were estimated at 938km/h (583mph) and 3540km (2200 miles) respectively. As a bomber a crew of four would have been accommodated and armament would have included 12 1000lb bombs and 40 5in rockets in the bay and under the wings.

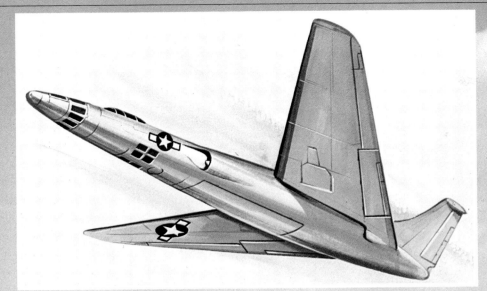

Artist's impression of the projected Convair XB-53, drawn from Convair Division material.

The A-45, actually the last aircraft to carry the original 'A' series designation, came from Martin but was subsequently redesignated XB-51. Two prototypes again were ordered, the first of which flew initially on 28 October 1949. Power was provided by three General Electric J47 turbojets, two in pods carried on the lower forward sides of the fuselage and one in the rear fuselage. The mid-mounted wings were swept back at 35 degrees and a 'T' tail was used. The crew comprised a pilot under a fighter-type

Above: WB-66D Destroyer, equipped to collect meteorological information over a battle area.

Douglas RB-66C version of the
Destroyer, with underfuselage and
underwing radomes, first flown on 29
October 1955.

EB-66B Destroyer, used in Vietnam as
electronic countermeasures aircraft.

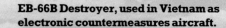

canopy and a navigator in a cabin to the rear.

By the time the two prototypes had been handed over to the USAF for testing, the United States was at war in Korea. Now the USAF urgently required new light attack bombers and found them in the form of the Canberra and B-66 Destroyer. As neither were new designs they offered a quick and safe way out. As for the XB-51, this was abandoned.

The Canberra, which became the B-57 when produced in the United States by Martin, has already been mentioned. The Destroyer was basically a derivative of the Navy's Skywarrior and yet actually managed to beat it into service. The initial version was the RB-66A, five of which were produced as four-camera trial tactical reconnaissance aircraft. Each was powered by two Allison J71-A-9 turbojet engines car-

ried in underwing pods. The first flew initially on 28 June 1954, marking the first flight of a Destroyer.

The bomber version of the Destroyer was the B-66B, 72 being completed. The first was flown on 4 January 1955. The Allison J71-A-11 engines of the early examples were superseded by 4627kg (10,200lb)st J71-A-13s. Armament comprised conventional and nuclear weapons carried in the bay and two 20mm cannon carried in a tail ball-turret and remotely controlled by one of the three crew. Maximum speed was 1013km/h (630mph). Those entered service from 10 March 1956.

The major production version of the Destroyer was the RB-66B, basically an RB-66A but carrying five cameras, photoflash bombs and cartridges. B-66B engines and tail armament were fitted. The first of the 145 built was delivered to the USAF on 1 Febru-

ary 1956, making this the first production version to enter service. A further 36 Destroyers were built as RB-66C all-weather electronic reconnaissance aircraft and a similar number of WB-66Ds were produced. The WB-66D was the first weather reconnaissance aircraft to be built as new. During the conflict in Vietnam a small number of B-66Bs were converted into EB-66B ECM aircraft and some RB-66Cs became EB-66Cs with ECM. These were the final Destroyers in USAF operational service.

Today in many air forces, the attack aircraft is represented by some of the most up-to-date combat planes. These not only serve worldwide but have been or are being manufactured in many different countries, a far cry from the old days. However, not included here are the fighter-bombers fully covered in *Jet Fighters*. Only brief mention of each type is given as these are

EMBRAER EMB-326GB/AT-26 Xavante light attack/trainer built in Brazil.

British Strikemaster Mk 82 in service
with the Sultan of Oman's Air Force,
armed with bombs and rockets.

Left: An early Panavia Tornado flying fast and low through mountain valleys carrying eight 1,000lb bombs, electronic countermeasures pods and auxiliary fuel tanks.

not jet bombers in the traditionally accepted sense.

From Argentina comes the twin turbo-prop-engined FMA Pucará, a lightweight close support and counterinsurgency aircraft with the ability to carry up to 1686kg (3717lb) of weapons in addition to its two fixed cannon. Maximum speed at an all-up weight of 5500kg (12,125lb) is 500km/h (310mph). From its South American neighbor Brazil comes the EMBRAER AT-26 Xavante, just one license-built version of the Italian Aermacchi MB326 jet trainer and

Tornado armed with an underfuselage munitions dispenser.

ground attack aircraft. The MB326/AT-26 is a typical example of many dual purpose aircraft in this category, another being the British BAe Strikemaster that was exported to 10 countries.

Europe is represented by four types.

IDS Tornado in service with the German Air Force and seen here at the weapon conversion unit at Erding.

One is the two-seat Panavia Tornado Mach 2+ multipurpose combat aircraft, now becoming operational in Britain, West Germany and Italy as those countries' first swing-wing aircraft. Capable of many roles including close air support, interdiction and naval strike, it can carry up to 9072kg (20,000lb) of weapons.

The other three European aircraft are the Mach 1.6 SEPECAT Jaguar tactical support aircraft, built by France and Britain and exported and capable of carrying up to 4763kg (10,500lb) of weapons; the broadly

Below: An IDS Tornado (interdictor strike version) refuels another Tornado using a buddy-buddy refueling system.

French air force Jaguar A, flown by the 11th Escadre de Chasse.

Jaguar International for Oman, the export version of the Jaguar with the most powerful engines to enhance performance and maneuverability.

RAF Jaguar T.Mk 2 two-seat operational trainer carrying four 1,000lb bombs during rough field take-off trials.

The combat-proven British Aerospace
Harrier GR.Mk 3 lifts off.

similar 1160km/h (721mph) Romanian/ Yugoslav SOKO/CNIAR Orao/IAR-93 close support aircraft, powered by Rolls-Royce Viper engines; and the BAe Harrier V/STOL close support aircraft capable of carrying more than 2270kg (5000lb) of stores. The US-developed AV-8B Harrier II derivative for the USMC and RAF has greater performance and a heavier weapon load and is scheduled for service from late 1983.

Soviet aircraft in this category are represented by several types from Mikoyan and Sukhoi. The Mach 1.5 Mikoyan MiG-27 (NATO *Flogger*) is a single-seat swing-wing ground attack aircraft derived from the MiG-23 fighter. The new Sukhoi Su-25 (NATO *Frogfoot*) single-seat close support aircraft has a similar role to the USAF's A-10A but has its engines carried in the wing-roots. The maximum weapon load of the

Right: US-developed AV-8B Harrier II in USMC markings and carrying bombs and air-to-air missiles.

Below: As the attacks on Port Stanley airfield and Goose Green on 1 May 1982 proved, the Sea Harrier is more than just a naval fighter and reconnaissance V/STOL aircraft.

Su-25, which became operational in 1983, is unknown: that for the MiG-27 is 3000kg (6615lb).

The single-seat Mach 1.6 Sukhoi Su-7B (NATO *Fitter-A*), which dates from the 1950s, is still in use in many countries, as are the much newer Mach 2+ Su-17/20/22 (NATO *Fitter*) swing-wing attack aircraft built for the Soviet forces and for export.

Below: Egyptian Air Force Sukhoi Su-7BM, one of forty in operational use.

The most powerful Soviet attack aircraft is the Su-24 (NATO *Fencer*), also using swing-wings and accommodating a crew of two seated side-by-side. Maximum speed and weapon load are Mach 2+ and approximately 8000kg (17,635lb) respectively.

The United States has several aircraft that fit into this category, despite the General Dynamics F-111 not being included as this tactical fighter is covered in *Jet Fighters*. Currently the most prominent is the Fairchild Republic A-10A Thunderbolt II, which became operational in 1977 as a close support aircraft capable of 706km/h (439mph) without externally-carried weapons. Armament comprises a General Electric GAU-8/A Avenger 30mm seven-barrel cannon in the nose and up to 7250kg (16,000lb) of ex-

Left: Far more formidable than the Su-7B is the Su-20, one of two export versions of the Soviet Su-17 *Fitter*.

Right: One of 586 Fairchild Republic A-10A Thunderbolt II close support aircraft delivered to the USAF by the beginning of 1982.

Below: A Maverick air-to-surface missile about to be loaded on an A-10A.

Bottom: A-10As of the 353rd Tactical Fighter Squadron, USAF, prepare to attack during the US/Egyptian exercise Bright Star 82.

The USMC's two-seat Rockwell International OV-10D, 17 of which were produced as night observation and surveillance aircraft from OV-10As Armament capability is retained.

ternal stores. This aircraft, which was selected for service in preference to the Northrop A-9A, is powered by two rear fuselage-mounted turbofan engines.

The Rockwell International OV-10 Bronco is a two-seat lightweight multipurpose counter-insurgency aircraft used by the USMC and exported. It is powered by two turboprop engines, has a maximum speed of 463km/h (288mph) and can carry 1633kg (3600lb) of weapons on fuselage attachment points.

Three US aircraft of fighter configuration but designed for interdiction/strike roles are the McDonnell Douglas F-15E Enhanced Eagle, the General Dynamics F-16XL and the Northrop F/A-18L. The former, based on the USAF's Eagle air superiority fighter, will carry a weapon load of 10,885kg (24,000lb). The F-16XL is an advanced technology version of the Fighting Falcon and

Northrop's rival to the A-10A was the A-9A, but this was not ordered into production. Reports suggest that the Soviet _Frogfoot_ could be similar.

Formerly known as Strike Eagle, the F-15E Enhanced Eagle will be capable of day, night and all-weather attacks.

will carry up to 6803kg (15,000lb) of stores. The F/A-18L, based on the US Navy Hornet, can carry a load weighing 9072kg (20,000lb). All are also capable of fighter roles, but none as yet is in service.

The last aircraft to be mentioned comes from China and was also covered in *Jet Fighters.* Known in that country as the Qiangjiji-5, to others as the Nanchang Q-5 and to NATO as *Fantan-A,* it is a Mach 1.35 fighter-bomber also used for air defense. It is mentioned in this book as its Chinese name means Attack aircraft 5. It is, with the F-111 from the USA, one of a very small

number of non-strategic aircraft with an internal weapons bay for conventional or nuclear bombs. Other weapons can be carried underwing. Q-5s currently serve with the Air Force of the People's Liberation Army and with the Pakistan Air Force.

Four Nanchang Q-5 *Fantan-A*s strike out across mountainous terrain during low-level flying training.

The rear cockpit of the F-15E is occupied by a specialist officer, who operates targeting avionics.

15: BREAKING BARRIERS

20001

The 1940s were not over before attention was turned in the United States to the possibility of producing a jet bomber with supersonic performance. The leap from the existing subsonic jet bomber types to an aircraft with supersonic performance took several more years but the resulting aircraft was not merely a Mach 1 but a Mach 2 bomber.

In 1948 Convair had flown its Model 7002 (XF-92A) as the world's first true delta-winged aircraft. This wing configuration became a standard feature of Convair aircraft for a long period thereafter, but one of its first applications was for a proposed supersonic bomber. This won a USAF design study competition of 1949. Two years later the project was assigned the designation XB-58 by the USAF, together with a contract to continue design of the 'generalized' bomber.

By then Boeing too had entered the competition to provide the USAF with its first supersonic bomber. From April 1951 the company produced many designs under its model 701 type number and actually re-

This view of the B-58A Hustler shows clearly the bomber's delta wings, engine layout and the single compartment fuel/ weapon pod carried under the fuselage.

Previous page: North American Valkyrie during low-altitude supersonic cruise flight, with wingtips folded at 25 degrees.

ceived the official USAF designation XB-59 for its project. However, no prototype was ever built by Boeing, although progressive configurations included those with swept-back and delta wings.

In August 1952 Convair received the MX-1964 contract to produce the B-58 under the new weapon system management concept, making Convair responsible for managing the development of all B-58 systems with the

The Convair B-58A Hustler was the world's first production supersonic bomber, entering USAF service in 1959 and becoming operational the following year.

The General Dynamics FB-111A was developed from the F-111 tactical fighter. As this photograph shows, the F-111 itself can carry a heavy bombload.

An early FB-111A/SRAM attack missile combination.

exception of the turbojet engines. The first of two XB-58 prototypes flew for the first time on 11 November 1956. These were followed by a second prototype, 11 further service test YB-58As and another 17 test aircraft (ordered in early 1957) including some in reconnaissance bomber configuration.

The B-58 itself had mid-mounted delta wings. Because of the high temperatures associated with Mach 2 flight, the heat and fatigue-resistant skin panels used on the wings and fuselage were constructed as a sandwich, with glassfiber/aluminum/stainless steel honeycomb between layers of metal. The bomber also made the first use of the escape capsule concept, in which the crew of three sat in individual capsules that

Below: General Dynamics proposed the conversion of F-111Ds and FB-111As into FB-111B/C penetration bombers, with new engines and greater wing span. This remained a project.

could be ejected in an emergency, thereby allowing ejection at supersonic speed. The first manned ejection took place in February 1962 and B-58s delivered without this system were subsequently modified. Armament comprised a radar-directed Vulcan 20mm multibarrel tail cannon and nuclear or conventional bombs carried inside a jettisonable underfuselage pod. The pod also carried the fuel for the outward journey. Subsequently a two-compartment pod was developed, the lower fuel-carrying section being jettisoned when empty and the upper carrying fuel, a bomb and electronic equipment. Fuel for the home journey was carried in wing tanks. Maximum take-off weight of the B-58A production aircraft was 73,935kg (163,000lb), maximum speed 2229km/h (1385mph) and range 3862km (2400 miles).

The first eight of the 86 production B-58s built were each powered by four General Electric J79-GE-1 turbojets. The standard engines thereafter were four 7076kg (15,600lb)st with afterburning J79-GR-5 series turbojets. In addition, 10 service test aircraft were brought up to production standard for service in the bomber role and

The underside of a camouflaged FB-111A with SRAM. The angle of wingsweep varies according to the type and number of weapons attached to external pylons.

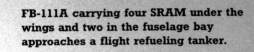

FB-111A carrying four SRAM under the
wings and two in the fuselage bay
approaches a flight refueling tanker.

Valkyrie during high-altitude and high-speed cruising flight, with wingtips folded at 65 degrees.

eight became TB-58A dual-control trainers.

The B-58A, known as the Hustler, was delivered to the USAF's 43rd Bombardment Wing stationed at Carswell AFB, Texas, from late 1959, becoming operational in March of the following year. By August three squadrons were operational. The 305th Wing received Hustlers in 1961. The bomber remained operational throughout the 1960s.

This view of Valkyrie shows clearly the layout of the six turbojet engines and the rectangular-section air duct forward.

It was to Carswell AFB that the General Dynamics FB-111A two-seat strategic bomber was first delivered in October 1969, to equip the 340th Bomb Group. This Group provided training for the operational Wings.

The FB-111A was a strategic bomber development of the F-111 swing-wing tactical fighter, developed to supersede both the early versions of the Boeing B-52 Stratofortress and the Hustler. Of the 253 planned for service, only 76 were in fact completed. The first of these flew initially on 13 July 1968 and all had been built by 1971. A larger and more powerful derivative known as the FB-111H and also FB-111B/C conversions were also considered when the B-1 bomber was cancelled, but these were never built.

Right: Roll-out of the first Rockwell International B-1 strategic bomber prototype at Palmdale, California, on 26 October 1974.

The FB-111A accommodates a crew of two side-by-side and is powered by two 9230kg (20,350lb)st Pratt & Whitney TF30-P-7 with afterburning turbofan engines. The 60 aircraft that currently equip five medium-range bomber squadrons of Strategic Air Command (three aircraft are also in reserve) can each carry six SRAM missiles, four underwing and two in the internal weapons bay, or up to 14,288kg (31,500lb) of conventional weapons. Maximum speed is Mach 2.5 and range 6598km (4100 miles) while carrying external fuel tanks.

The first full-range strategic bomber developed as a B-52 replacement was the incredible North American XB-70 Valkyrie. A huge delta-winged aircraft with 12 elevons and fold-down wingtips for high-speed cruise, large foreplanes and powered by six 14,060kg (31,000lb)st General Electric YJ93-GE-3 turbojet engines, it could cruise to and from the target at a constant Mach 3. Unrefueled range was approximately 12,230km (7600 miles). First flown on 21 September 1964, the bomber was cancelled before production.

The second supersonic B-52 full-range replacement was produced by Rockwell International as the Mach 2+ B-1 low-altitude

By July 1976 three B-1 prototypes had accumulated a total of more than 200 hours flying, achieving speeds in excess of Mach 2.

B-1 prototype with wings fully spread.

penetration bomber. The first swing-wing prototype flew for the first time on 23 December 1974. Two hundred and forty-four were to have been delivered to SAC by 1981, but production was cancelled by President Carter in 1977 after four prototypes had been completed.

President Carter's cancellation of the B-1 in favor of cruise missile development led to proposals for a cruise missile carrier, one obvious answer being a B-1 derivative. However, the Air Force Scientific Advisory Board suggested that a new USAF strategic bomber should be capable of other bombing roles in addition to carrying cruise missiles and in 1981 President Reagan announced that the USAF would receive 100

B-1 prototype in camouflage, with wings swept.

derivative Rockwell International B-1Bs from 1985 to 1988.

The B-1B is also a swing-wing aircraft, but has a designed maximum speed of Mach 1.25. Power is provided by four 13,608kg (30,000lb)st General Electric F101-GE-102 augmented turbofan engines carried in pairs below the wing center-section. This 12,000km (7455 mile) unrefueled-range bomber will be capable of carrying eight ALCM or 24 SRAM missiles, or nuclear or conventional bombs internally, and similar weapons on external underfuselage attachments. When carrying conventional 500lb Mk 82 bombs only, 128 can be carried internally and externally.

Soviet supersonic bomber capability was introduced with the Tupolev Tu-22, known to NATO as *Blinder*. First seen in public during the Aviation Day celebration of 1961, it has mid-mounted swept wings and is powered by two turbojet engines positioned above the rear fuselage each side of the vertical tail. As with the US Hustler, to which it could be compared, *Blinder* car-

The B-1B will incorporate very advanced avionics. Technological advances will reduce its radar signature to just one percent of that of the USAF's current Stratofortress.

ries a crew of three in tandem cockpits. However, *Blinder* has a maximum speed and unrefuelled radius of action of approximately Mach 1.4 and 3100km (1925 miles) respectively.

It is believed that approximately 250 Tu-22s were built in several versions. The *Blinder-A* reconnaissance-bomber carries bombs in the weapons bay. *Blinder-B* is capable of carrying the *Kitchen* nuclear air-to-surface strategic missile and *Blinder-C* was deployed as a maritime reconnaissance aircraft but now has likely electronic intelligence or ECM capabilities. *Blinder-D* is a tandem cockpit trainer. The Soviet long-range air force currently operates approximately 125 *Blinder A*s and *B*s as bombers and 15 *Blinder-C*s for reconnaissance. Naval Aviation currently deploys approximately 40 *Blinder-A*s and a handful of *Blinder-C*s. Bombers are also operational with Iraq (9) and Libya (7), and the Soviet Union and Libya use *Blinder-D*.

Undoubtedly the most important strategic bomber to enter service in the past decade has been the Soviet Tupolev Tu-22M, its designation indicating that it was intended as a *Blinder* replacement. However, there are no similarities between the two types in terms of configuration or performance, although *Backfire* (NATO name) has

**Tupolev Tu-22M *Backfire-B*
photographed by a Swedish Air Force
pilot.**

two turbofan engines mounted side by side
in the rear fuselage.

First flown in prototype form in 1971, the
Soviet strategic long-range air force operates approximately 100 *Backfire-A*s and improved *Backfire-B*s as strategic bombers.

Naval Aviation currently has about 80 for
attack and maritime reconnaissance roles.
Backfire continues in production. These
bombers operate in the European area and
over the Atlantic, but can also reach the
United States with flight refueling. An advanced version of *Backfire* has also been
flown.

Backfire is in the mold of the latest
bombers, having swing wings. It has a max-

imum take-off weight of approximately
122,500kg (270,000lb) and a maximum
speed of Mach 2. Its armament can comprise twin radar-directed 23mm cannon in a
tail position and up to 12,000kg (26,450lb) of
bombs or a *Kitchen* missile. A decoy missile of the US Quail type may have been
developed for Soviet bombers. *Backfire*
can fly to a target approximately 5470km
(3400 miles) from base without flight refueling.

The latest Soviet bomber is also from the
Tupolev design bureau and is known to
NATO as *Blackjack*. This is said to be a
manned swing-wing penetration bomber
nearly half as big again as *Backfire* and
larger than the USAF's future B-1B. It is capable of a maximum speed of Mach 2.3 and
has an unrefueled range of 13,500km (8400
miles). Armament may include cruise missiles or other nuclear or conventional
weapons up to approximately 16,330kg
(36,000lb). *Blackjack* could be operational
by 1986.

Two Soviet supersonic bombers that
failed to reach production were the

***Blinder* twin-turbojet supersonic bomber
in high-speed flight.**

The TSR 2 was capable of fully automatic attacks from high or low level.

Myasishchev M-52 (NATO *Bounder*) of 1958, a 2000km/h (1243mph) strategic bomber of limited range, and the four-engined supersonic cruise bomber built in the 1970s by Sukhoi. The latter had the look and probably the speed of the US XB-70.

A British supersonic attack bomber and reconnaissance aircraft that could have become operational in the 1960s was the BAC TSR 2. At the time of its first flight in September 1964 this was probably the most formidable aircraft of its type in the world. A two-seater, it had a speed of Mach 2.05-2.5 and a range with underwing tanks of about 2780km (1727 miles). Its avionics would have allowed completely automatic high and low level attacks without visual reference.

France joined the USA and USSR in having its own supersonic strategic bomber during the 1960s, with the delivery from 1963 of 62 production delta-winged Dassault Mirage IV-As. Based on an enlarged Mirage III configuration, the prototype first flew on 17 June 1959. Two-seat IV-As, each with two 7200kg (15,873lb)st with afterburning SNECMA Atar 9K-50 turbojets, performed France's nuclear deterrent role until land and submarine-based missiles took over, thereafter becoming low-level tactical strike aircraft. Today the French Air Force operates 34 Mirage IV-As, each carrying a nuclear weapon recessed into the underfuselage, or 16 1000lb bombs, or four Martel missiles. Maximum speed is 2340km/h (1454mph) and tactical radius 1240km (770 miles). Four more are used for training, and six bombers and four reconnaissance conversions are in reserve, the latter carrying the associated equipment for its new role in a large pod.

What future has the bomber? There is no doubt that the bomber of the 1980s is a vastly expensive aircraft, probably only affordable in any quantity to the 'superpowers.' It is more vulnerable to destruction than a submarine in the strategic role, but more versatile, allowing its use in limited and major conflicts and giving strategists the choice at any stage of carrying conventional or nuclear weapons. Has the bomber a future? Only time will tell.

In this photograph the TSR 2 has its undercarriage lowered. The all-moving vertial tail surface and horizontal 'tailerons' for pitch and roll control are prominent.

Main picture: The Mirage IV-A supersonic strategic bomber (left) stands beside other Dassault-Breguet combat aircraft in the latter 1960s.

The TSR 2 made its last flight on 31 March 1965. Here the aircraft is seen on display at Cranfield in 1967.

Britain's only supersonic attack bomber, the TSR 2, in level flight.

Above: A Mirage IV-A takes off using JATO units. Large jettisonable fuel tanks are carried under the wings.

A Mirage IV-A takes on fuel from a French Air Force Boeing C-135F tanker.

The Mirage IV-A as it now appears, in full camouflage for low-level missions.

This photograph of a Mirage IV-A in level flight shows the nuclear weapon semi-recessed under the fuselage.

The crew of a Vulcan B.Mk 2 leave their aircraft.

Mirage 2000 prototype escort a Mirage 4000.

Page numbers in italics refer to illustrations

F

Falkland Islands 208, 229, 234,
    244, 253
Fiat company 51
fighter aircraft 8–157 *passim*, 202,
    205, 242, 290, 291
fighter bombers 205, 278
flight refueling 36, 136, 188, 205,
    220, 229, *230*, 238, 242,
    259, *281*, *312*
flying wing concept 190, *191–3*,
    193
Folland Aircraft Company 129
forward swept wing 14, *68–9*, 69,
    116
France
    Canberra used by 217
    engine development in 38, 39,
        64, 93, 202–4
fuel economy 209, 258

G

Galland, Adolf 8, 22
General Electric Company 176
German air force 16–17, 21, 24,
    142, *281*
Germany, engine development in
    9–12, 16–18, 20–4,
    168–173
Gloster aircraft company 208
Griffith, Dr A A 8, 57
Grumman Corporation 84, 248

H

Hahn, Max 10
Handley Page company 208, 213,
    219, 229
Hawker aircraft company 97, 209
Heinkel, Ernst 8–11, 16–18, 23
Heinkel company 8, 9–10, 16–17,
    23–4, 171
Hindustan Aeronautics Ltd 132
Hispano-Suiza company 202

I

Ilyushin, Sergei 200
Indian air forces 97, 99, 156, *212*,
    215
Integrated Operational
    Intelligence System 248
Iraqi air force 146, 200, 266, 308
Israeli air force 42, 121, 125, 141,
    146, 154, 204

J

Junkers aircraft company 11, 196

K

Klimov, V Ya 196

L

Leduc, René 66
Leist, Professor 11
Ling-Temco-Vought 91, 250
Lockheed Corporation 27, 57, 188
low altitude bombing system 229
Lyulka, Arkhip M 196

M

McDonnell Aircraft Corporation
    74, 80–1
McDonnel Douglas 81
maritime reconnaissance 266, 271,
    308, 309
Martin (Glenn L) company 178,
    184–5, 186, 193, 213, 278
Messerschmitt company 16–17, 23
Mikoyan Gurevich bureau 43
Milch, E 10, 11, 16
missiles
    Polaris 208, 229
    AGM-20 Quail decoy 263, 264
missiles, air-to-air
    Acrid 150
    Alkali 115, 116
    Anab 116, 121
    Apex 150, 151
    Aphid 150, 151
    Ash 121
    Atoll, Advanced Atoll 117
    Falcon 38, 104, 108, *126–7*, 127,
        142
    Firestreak 66, 94, 136, 137
    Genie 38, 104, 110
    Matra 92, 123
    Matra 530, Super 530, 92, 126,
        151, 154
    Matra Magic 93, 99, 151, 154
    Phoenix 88
    Red Top 94, 137
    Shafrir 154
    Sidewinder 75, 76, 81, *83*,
        86–103 *passim*, *98*, 109,
        110, 126–8 *passim*, 142,
        146, 149, 151, 156, *156*
    Skyflash 142, 149, 156, *156*
    Sparrow 75, 76, 81, 88, 91, 109,
        142, *143*
missiles, air-to-ground 97, 99,
    110, 117
    A.S.30 215
    Bell GAM-63 Rascal 187, 188
    Bull Pup 248
    Kangaroo (Sov.) 269, 271
    Kelt (Sov.) 266, *266*
    Martel 253, 310

Maverick *289*
    Shrike 110
    SRAM *264–5*, 265, *302–3*, 308
missiles, anti-radiation 110, 141,
    208, 248
missiles, anti-ship
    Exocet 93, 253
    Kennel, Kingfisher, Kipper
        (Sov.) 266
missiles, strategic stand-off 218
    AGM-28 Hound Dog 263, *263*,
        264
    ALCM *257*, 307, 308
        AGM-86B 265, *265*
        AGM-109H Tomahawk *260*
    Blue Steel *226*, 229, 234, *234*
    Kitchen (Sov.) 271, 308, 309
    Skybolt *225*, 229, 264
missiles, surface-to-air 220
    Bloodhound 66
    Regulus 242
    Standard 110
    V750K (Sov.) *Guideline* 220
Mitsubishi company 51, 88, 142

N

New Zealand air force 215
North American aircraft company
    186, 193, 238
    X-15 program 262
North Korean air force 53, 200
Northrop aircraft company 56, 80,
    178, 193
nuclear weapons, aircraft
    carrying 38, 75, 97, 200,
        208, 218, 229, 234, 238,
        239, 244, 245, 248, 263,
        266, 269, 271, 278, 291,
        301, 308, 310
    tactical use of 191, 215, 253

O

Ohain, Hans Joachim P von 8, 10,
    11, 16, 17, 166, 170
Oman air force *279*

P

Pakistan air force 96, 218, 291
Petter, W E W 213
Pohl, Professor Robert 10
Polish air force 200, *288*
Power Jets Ltd 8, 12, 13

R

Ramjet aircraft 30, 66, 196
Rebeski, Ing Hans 164

INDEX

ACKNOWLEDGMENTS

Photographs are from the author's collection except as listed below:

Air BP: 8
Air Portraits: 65, 66
British Aerospace/Paul Cullerne: 221, 222, 223, 224
Austin J Brown: 94 (bottom), 119
Bill Hobson: 172, 197, 275
Denis Hughes: 111, 115, 116, 117, 150–1, 198–9, 266–7, 288
Imperial War Museum: 164–5, 168–9, 170–1, 172–3
MAP: 116–17
Ministry of Defence (UK): 230–1, 254, 267, 271
Matthew Nathan: 9, 10 (both), 11, 19, 22–3
Polish Air Force: 288
Royal Air Force Museum, Hendon: 6–7, 12–13, 20–1, 95, 206–07, 208–09, 210–11
SIRPA: 312, 313
Bob Snyder: 17, 26–7, 30, 30–1, 52–3, 56 (top), 97, 128–9
Tass: 309
US Air Force: 34, 36, 36–7, 48, 180–1, 182–3, 192, 214–15
US Navy: 70–1, 75, 249
Gordon S Williams: 44–5, 186–7, 237